He who binds himself to a joy
Doth the winged life destroy;
But he who kisses the joy as it flies
Lives in eternity's sunrise

William Blake

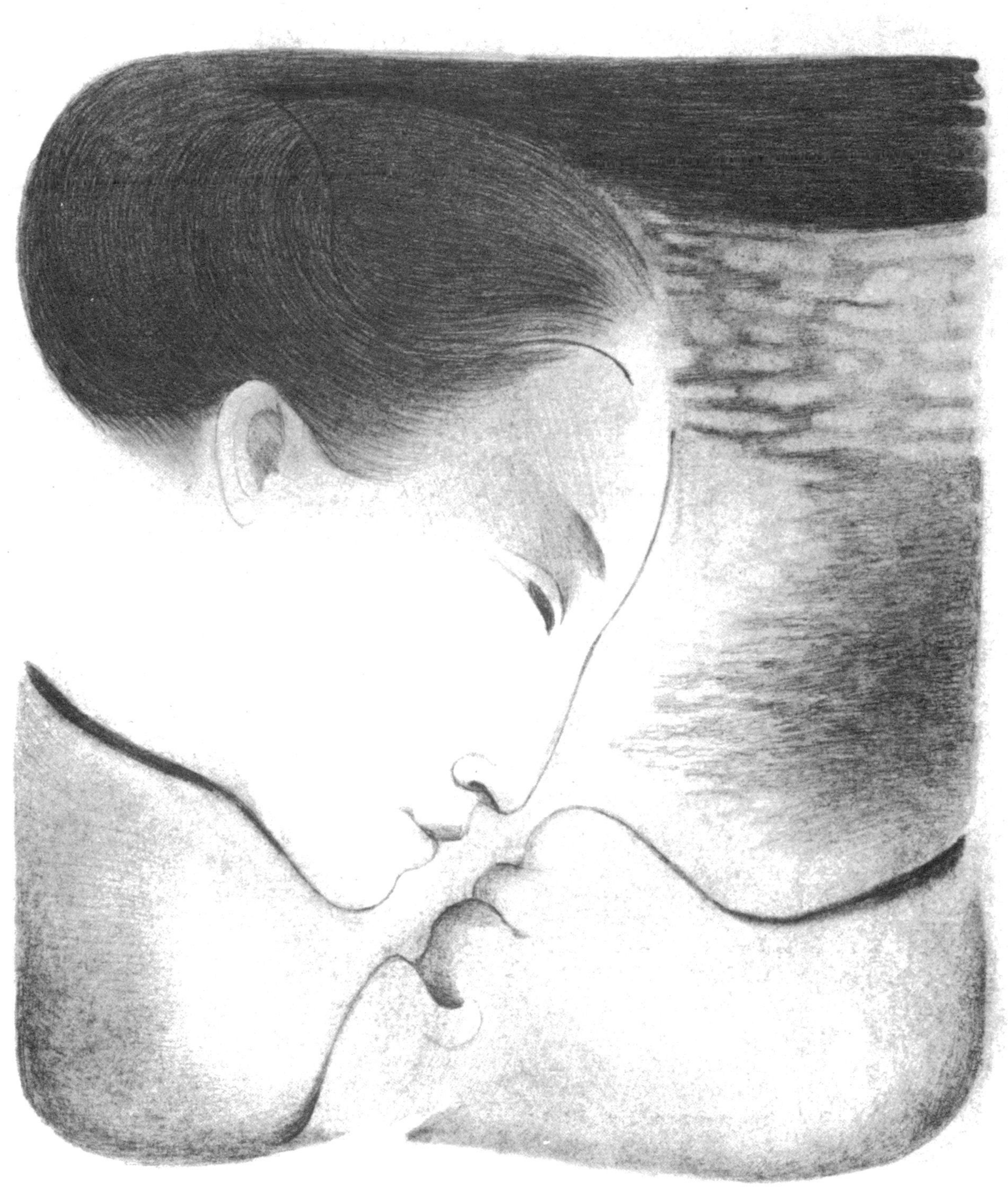

SENSUAL CEREMONY

A Contemporary Tantric Guide To Sexual Intimacy

Kenneth Ray Stubbs, Ph.D.

Illustrated by
Richard Stodart

Secret Garden
Larkspur, CA

Also by Kenneth Ray Stubbs, Ph.D.

Sacred Orgasms: Teachings from the Heart

Tantric Massage: An Illustrated Manual For Meditative Sexuality

Romantic Interludes: A Sensuous Lovers Guide

The Clitoral Kiss: A Fun Guide to Oral Sex, Oral Massage, and Other Oral Delights

Published by **Secret Garden**
P.O. Box 67-CCA
Larkspur, California 94977-0067

Printed in the United States of America

Illustrations: Richard Stodart
Cover: Richard Stodart
Author's Photo: Jim Dennis

ISBN 0-939263-10-6

A Word of Caution

The purpose of this book is to educate. It is not intended to give medical or psychological therapy. Whenever there is concern about physical or emotional illness, a qualified professional should be consulted.

The authors, illustrators, and the publisher shall have neither liability nor responsibility to any person or entity with respect to any loss, damage, injury, or ailment caused or alleged to be caused directly or indirectly by the information or lack of information in this book.

Dedicated to

Sun Dancer

Fly free, my friend

Acknowledgments

Sensual Ceremony evolved out of my experience of giving over three hundred Secret Garden Ceremonies to friends, lovers, and strangers-becoming-friends. These people and ceremonies are special moments in my life.

The Secret Garden Ceremony might never have evolved were it not for Sun Dancer. He was the catalyst when the ceremony was only in my imagination. His friendship is both precious and auspicious for me.

Without Chyrelle D. Chasen this manuscript might have sat in storage another ten years. Thank you for your loving support.

Richard Stodart, the illustrator, embodies a sensual spirit in his he/art. I feel blessed.

Sandy Trupp, friend and publishing advisor, is always an inspiration.

There are many others to whom I deeply grateful: Bettina Suppe, Carole Merette, Clara Kerns, and Pam Johnson.

The Author

After teaching music in a Virgin Islands high school and sociology at the State University of New York, Kenneth Ray Stubbs, Ph.D., moved to San Francisco. There he became a certified masseur in 1973 and later a certified sexologist.

The Secret Garden Ceremony developed out of his experiences in massage and various forms of meditation. For over fifteen years Ray gave Secret Garden Ceremonies and led seminars on sensuality/ sexuality/spirituality throughout North America and Europe.

He now devotes his time to writing and publishing books emphasizing the reintegration of sexuality and spirituality.

The Illustrator

Richard Stodart is a native of Trinidad, West Indies and a Canadian citizen. In addition to figurative work he is currently developing a series of twelve abstract paintings about man's relationship to nature. He can be reached at his studio: Rte. 3, Box 142, Burgess, Virginia 22432.

CONTENTS

INVITATION 9

INTRODUCTION

1. Touching The Heart: Ceremonial Sensual Pleasuring 13

2. Kissing The Joy As It Flies: Giving The Gift 17

THE SECRET GARDEN CEREMONY

3. Ritual Accouterments: Accessories 29

4. The Inner Garden: Guided Imagery 35

5. Sensual Communion: Feeding 41

6. Ceremonial Waters: Bathing 55

7. Temple of the Spirit: Massage 71

TANTRIC EXPLORATIONS

8. Equanimity: Solo Meditations 83

9. Energy Dance: Mutual Meditations 93

EPILOGUE 111

INVITATION

A candle flame radiating

A finger resting

A peacock feather caressing

A mango melting

A stream of warm water searching

Arms embracing

Becoming One

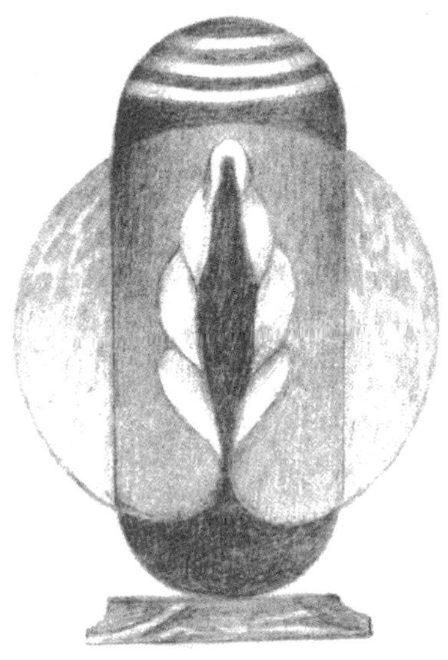

INTRODUCTION

1 Touching The Heart
Ceremonial Sensual Pleasuring

Ceremony is presence
It is being
rather than doing or having
It is attentive awareness

Ceremony is purposeful spontaneity
It is flowing pattern
It is simple elegance

A ceremony is not
a mindless routine
though many ceremonial structures
have become this
A ceremony can be
in solitude
with another
or with many others
There is a conscious beginning and ending

In ceremony
there is a sense
of wholeness
of connection
of comm-union

In sensual ceremony
we embrace the senses
through presence
through ambiance

through touch
taste
fragrance
tone and timbre
color and form

A sensual ceremony is a special gift
It is a physical sharing
of warmth and caring
It is an expression of tenderness
Giving this gift of pleasure
we invite another
to be guided into the inner garden
Here, in the quiet of sanctuary
we nourish each sense
Here, the inner flower
awakens and blooms

Our softly spoken words
weave a meadow
In herbal waters
we bathe
Our fingers
squeeze drops of sweetness
from fresh fruit
Lullabying,
we embrace
Like island breezes
we caress with feathers
Glistening with oil
our hands dance

When each sense
is nurtured in gentleness
the heart is touched
and we experience joy
This is the underlying philosophy

ASCETICISM, HEDONISM, TANTRA

Generally there are two orientations
toward the body and the senses:
the ascetic and the hedonistic

The ascetic philosophy
views anything that is

pleasing to the senses
as obstructive/destructive
to human development
either in material or spiritual attainment
There can be
abstention / denial / sometimes self-inflicted discomfort
The accompanying attitude
may be one of
condescension or disgust
toward the body
The implication,
pleasures of the flesh
lack meaningfulness,
they are addictive,
there is no real contribution
to the individual and society
The assumption,
there is something
inherently negative/evil about the body
After yielding to temptation
one must seek atonement

At the opposite end,
the hedonistic philosophy
Here one intensely pursues
gratification of desires
There is a grasping attempt
to hoard/consume

There is a story
about how a monkey can be captured
The end of a coconut
is cut off
and a handful of rice placed inside
Finding the prize
the monkey reaches inside
to grasp the rice
However, to get the fist back through
the narrow opening,
the hand must first relax
and let go of the rice
Unwilling to cease its grasping,
the monkey becomes burdened
and is easily captured

It is as if
there are strings of attachment
binding a hedonist
to a desired object

Asceticism Hedonism Tantra

Without continued titillation
life becomes boring

Pointing a finger at such behavior
an ascetic would label a hedonist
indulgent / decadent / narcissistic

There is another path, *tantra*
This philosophy
neither damns nor craves
the body and the sense experiences
Rather than being obstacles,
the sensations/feelings
become the vehicles of self-realization and well-being

Tantra
a Sanskrit word
comes to us from some schools
of Buddhism and Hinduism
Translated sometimes from a derivation of *to weave*
sometimes a combination of
to expand and *to liberate*
Acceptance
is a central teaching
Embracing the sensory experiences,
surrendering consciously to the moment
we transcend
the world of attachment
Allowing the flow of feelings
we develop empathy
deepen intimacy
Our mindfulness, our meditations
transform the energies
of each experience,
liberating us
from the limitations of grasping and avoiding

Here we open ourself
to a reverence for beauty
An aesthetic appreciation
enriches the meaning of life
In tantra
we celebrate
the heart and the senses
In tantra
we are
at-one-ment

2 Kissing The Joy As It Flies
Giving The Gift

TRUST GUIDELINES

A sensual ceremony
is for anyone in our life
female or male
friend or lover
for whom we wish
to express our love

Simply present an invitation
Be open to receiving "no"

Communicate
verbally or non-verbally
explicitly or implicitly
the following guidelines

1. "If there is anything I am doing or providing
that you want more of,
let me know"
2. "If there is anything I am doing or providing
that is either uncomfortable or undesirable,
let me know"
3. "If there is anything that I am not doing or providing
that you want,
let me know"

4. "Regarding your requests,
if I am willing and able to fulfill them,
I will do so
If I am either unwilling or unable to,
I will let you know"
(Though the intention
in most of the sensual ceremonies here
is for the recipient to receive without giving back,
this is open to renegotiation)
5. "As much as possible,
allow yourself to experience
your sensations and your feelings"

Following these guidelines
means that both the giver and receiver
have choice
From freedom of choice,
joy and love flow
Having, making, and communicating choices
are the cornerstone of trust

THE FOUR LIMITATIONS

There are four psychological patterns
that can limit sensual ceremony

Spectatoring/Performing

If we keep our attention on
"Am I doing it right?" or "wrong?"
we are like a spectator
watching for a flaw in a performance on a stage
Our mind has a standard
that we have to live up to
When we are in this state
there is limited spontaneity and pleasure
Our awareness is on *should*
rather than our sensations and feelings

Judgments of Others

A judgment
is a perspective
that something a person is, does, or has
is not all right with me
Something is not OK
by my standard
Another is
too short
too fat
too rich
late too often
eats the wrong food
leaves the cap off the toothpaste...
We can have intimacy
to the extent
that we are willing to let go of our judgments
to the extent
we allow a person
to be exactly the way she/he is
and is not

Comparisons with the Past

In our mind
we can stretch a special moment into hours
make the sensations vibrant
deepen the profoundness of tender emotions
Reliving feelings
by remembering the events of the past
can be meaningful and beautiful

We rob ourself, however,
when we try to superimpose
the past on the present
We often find
the present does not live up to
that special event in the past
If we use the images from the past
to invalidate the present
we experience
neither value nor beauty

The Four Limitations

Expectations of the Future

When we have a standard
aimed at the future
we term it *expectation*
In our anticipation
we usually miss what is happening
in the moment
And then when the future arrives
and does not fulfill our expectations
our attention goes to what is lacking
In our emotional upset
we again miss the richness
of what is available
to our senses in the present

Letting Go

The extent to which
we can let go
of these limitations
is the extent to which
we can have pleasure in our life
Here are three suggestions

First, we can acknowledge
that we are the source of our
spectatoring/judgments/comparisons/expectations
Placing a cause elsewhere
we divert ourself
from the sensations/feelings
of the present
A second suggestion
is to not judge or reprimand ourself
Alternatively, we could view the situation as
an opportunity to learn about ourselves

Thirdly, enter a pleasuring activity
as ceremony
Perhaps attune yourself to the following teachings

TANTRIC TEACHINGS

To create a sense of ceremony,
we can be mindful of
receptivity
relaxation response
present-time experience

Receptivity means
there is no attachment
to the outcome of actions
Applying to both giving and receiving roles
this quality emphasizes
non-performance and non-demand
On the surface
receptivity may appear
to be the same as passivity
To the contrary,
receptivity requires
awareness
choice
It is very different
than *giving up*
than non-choice submissiveness
While receptivity emphasizes non-attachment
there is no opposition to
goals/directions
Were we to effort
to achieve a desired outcome, however,
we would blind ourself to many experiences
Efforting is opposite
to the nature of ceremony
Allowing, rather than striving,
is the key

Relaxation response means
there is a relatively calm body/mind
This is in contrast
to what we commonly call the fight-or-flight response
When we are being chased by a hungry tiger
we are not likely
to be conscious
of the jungle flowers' lovely fragrances
Physiologically speaking
performance anxiety and striving
create similar stress responses
as fleeing from the tiger
If we are to truly appreciate the senses
we must have an inner calm

Present-time experience means
we are not caught up
in our expectations of the future
or comparisons with the past
To experience pleasure
our attention must be in the present
This quality by no means suggests
that we deny or resist
our comparisons or expectations
Quite the contrary
with all comparisons and expectations
there are inner feeling experiences
which also include body sensations
In meditation
these sensations
can serve as attention focuses
To place our awareness in our sensations
is perhaps
the most powerful method
for coming back to present time,
for being present

The three qualities
receptivity, relaxation response, present-time experience
are essential facets
of ceremonial sensual pleasuring
When we *lose our senses*
or fail to appreciate our universe
these qualities can serve as signposts
to the tantric path

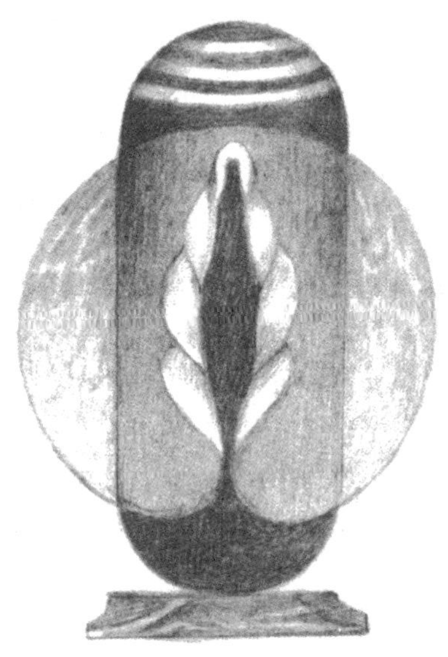

THE SECRET GARDEN CEREMONY

The Secret Garden Ceremony

If you wish to give a special gift
to express your love
to share communion
explore The Secret Garden Ceremony
Here one *gives*
while another *receives*
Similar to ancient tantric sexual rituals
in some ways,
the forms in this contemporary ceremony
may be more suitable
for many of us raised in Western culture

The following chapters present
the basic elements of The Secret Garden
Ceremony
guided imagery
feeding in the bath
bathing
massaging

Modify any part
according to your talents and desires
You may prefer
to make an element
a whole ceremony in itself
A sensual ceremony
may be for a few minutes
or several hours
Duration is not the essence

Many specific details follow
based on much trial and error
based on many sensual ceremonies
Allow the details
to serve you
when the information is relevant
Attachment to details
limits spontaneity
constricts the expression of essence
Non-attentiveness to details, however,
can result in non-ceremony
It's a delicate balance

You may mutually choose
with your partner
to be sexual, to be orgasmic
or not
before, during, or after
the ceremony

Enter the experience, however,
without predetermined goals
Allow each moment
each feeling
to unfold
without attachment
This is the tantric meditation

Overview

A few days prior to The Secret Garden Ceremony
have a pre-interview
with the recipient
This may be unnecessary
when giving to an intimate partner
if you already know
the likes/dislikes
possible food and skin allergies
The pre-interview is a time
to ask about feelings
and to arrange logistics:
schedules, baby sitter
roommates out of the apartment
no obligations afterward...

If this gift
is to be a surprise
make sure the recipient has
at least eight hours of unscheduled time

A few days before the ceremony
shop for the fruit
Market fruits often are insufficiently ripe

Anticipate at least one hour, possibly two or three
for the preparation immediately prior
to an extensive ceremony
The Secret Garden Ceremony itself, if given in total
could be three to six hours
First, the guided imagery
to calm the body/mind
to discover the inner garden
to create sanctuary
Following, in the bath
you nourish with fruits and sparkling nectar
in sensual communion
Next you bathe
in ceremonial waters

Then, anointing the temple of the spirit with oil
your hands massage
your beloved
Afterwards you might cuddle together
and breathe in unison
for another hour

A few days later
you might reflect together
sharing insights and special moments
A post-reflection, however,
definitely is not a post-game analysis
of *whys* and *should-haves*

For simplicity
the following instructions
usually use female gender pronouns
Modify as necessary

Most of all,
Enjoy!

3 RITUAL ACCOUTERMENTS
Accessories

MUSIC

The most conducive music
for most sensual ceremonies
is without lyrics
and usually without dominating rhythms
Words encourage thinking
which often is a distraction
from sensation and feeling experiences
And when the rhythm is obvious
we might follow the music's beat
rather than the receiver's

There is an increasing selection
of audio cassettes / compact disks
for calming and nourishing the body/mind
Possibilities include environmental recordings and
meditational music
While many classical selections
are very beautiful,
the moods, dynamics, and rhythms
frequently have a predominating influence
Experimentation is the key

Oils
Lotions
Soaps

OILS, LOTIONS, SOAPS

A good choice for massage oil
is a pure, unscented vegetable oil
Coconut oil is excellent
though it solidifies
at less-than-warm temperatures
Other possibilities are
plain almond oil, apricot kernel oil, and safflower oil
all of which can be purchased at
natural food stores and maybe supermarkets

You can add fragrances
to these oils
but not too much
Sometimes fragrance ingredients are irritating
to the skin and especially membranous tissues
Some consider mineral oil
to be unhealthy on or in our bodies
Its advantage is
it does not leave a rancid smell in sheets
Baby oil is simply mineral oil with fragrance added

Most lotions have a number of additives
and they usually evaporate or soak in
before you finish massaging
However, when mixed with oil
they create a wonderfully sensual texture
for hand and feet massage

Among soaps
the liquid variety may be easier to use
Usually they can be purchased at natural food stores
Some find peppermint liquid soap especially pleasing
but may be a little too mentholated
for the genital/anal areas

Unfortunately many of the commercial *love oils* and *love lotions*
leave much to be desired
especially if you were to ingest them
Use caution
if the ingredients are not listed
or if the listed ingredients are unfamiliar
or include additives or preservatives

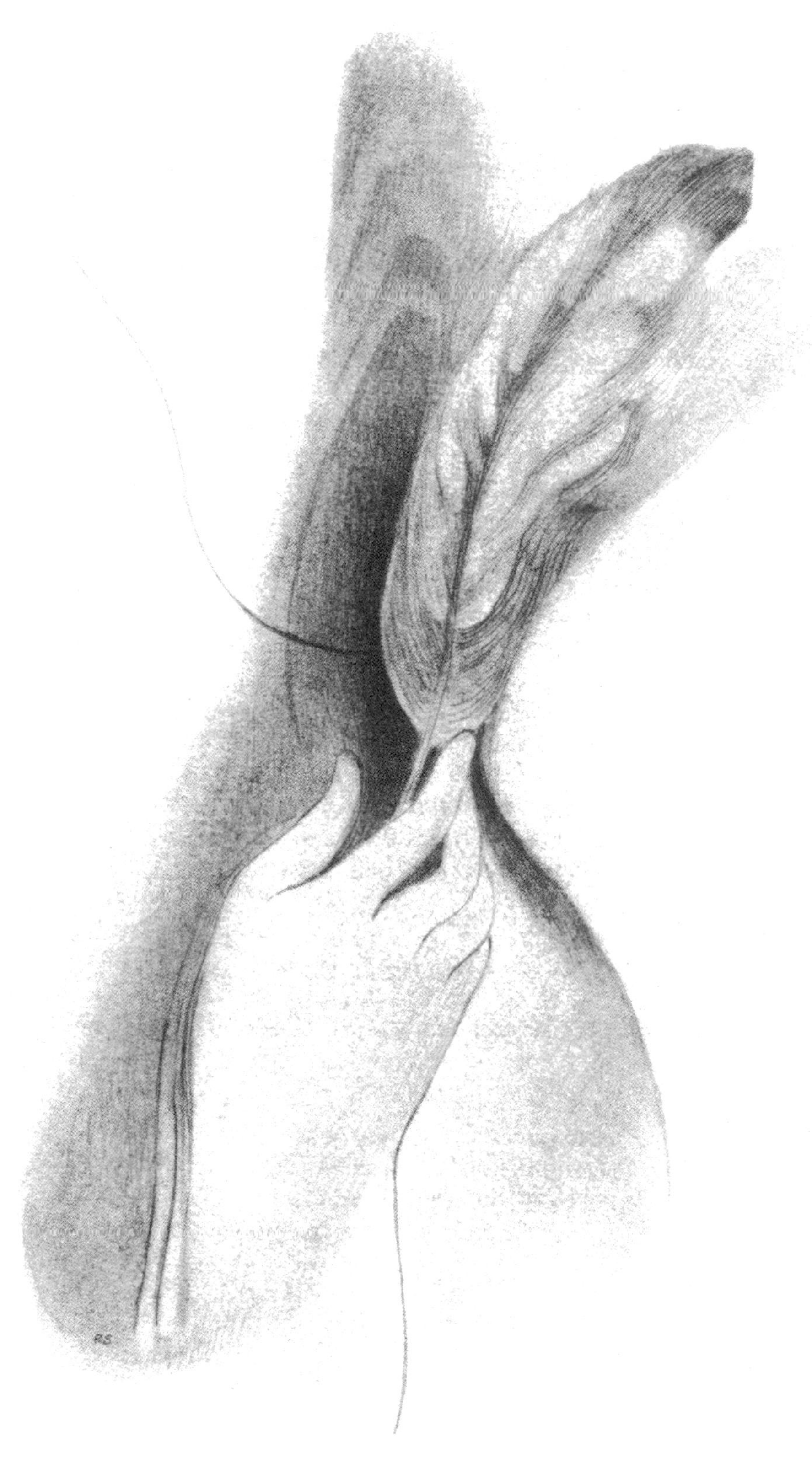

BATHING ACCESSORIES

A natural sponge and a loofa mitt
are favorites in the bath
Synthetic sponges may not feel aesthetically pleasing
When the loofa is of a mitt variety
(one side of loofa, the other side of cloth)
you can put one on each hand
These are often available at natural food stores
bath boutiques, and some cosmetic shops

Air pillow head rests for the bath
are great and are obtainable at bath boutiques

Hydrojets, either from portable or installed units
are fun but may be overpowering
in a nurturing ceremony

Rinsing with a hand-held container
— the rhythm
of pouring and then dipping for more water —
creates a calming trance
Since glass can break
and metal can be cumbersome and noisy
select a plastic container
perhaps about ten inches long
and four inches wide
Shower attachments that vary the water flow
are an alternative

FEATHERS AND FAVORITE FABRICS

Ostrich and peacock plumage
are especially pleasurable
Peacock feathers may be available
at shops that carry dried flowers,
while ostrich feathers may be difficult to find

Silky and furry fabrics
are other favorites

MASSAGE TABLES

When giving a massage,
for most, a massage table
is best
Alternatively
place a foam pad and sheet
on a sturdy dining room table
or a banquet table
(the kind with folding legs)

You may find other accouterments pleasing to the senses
browsing in shops specializing in oils and soaps
in bath shops
and in sensuous boutiques especially for lovers
Still,
your attentive presence
with your beloved
is the most important gift

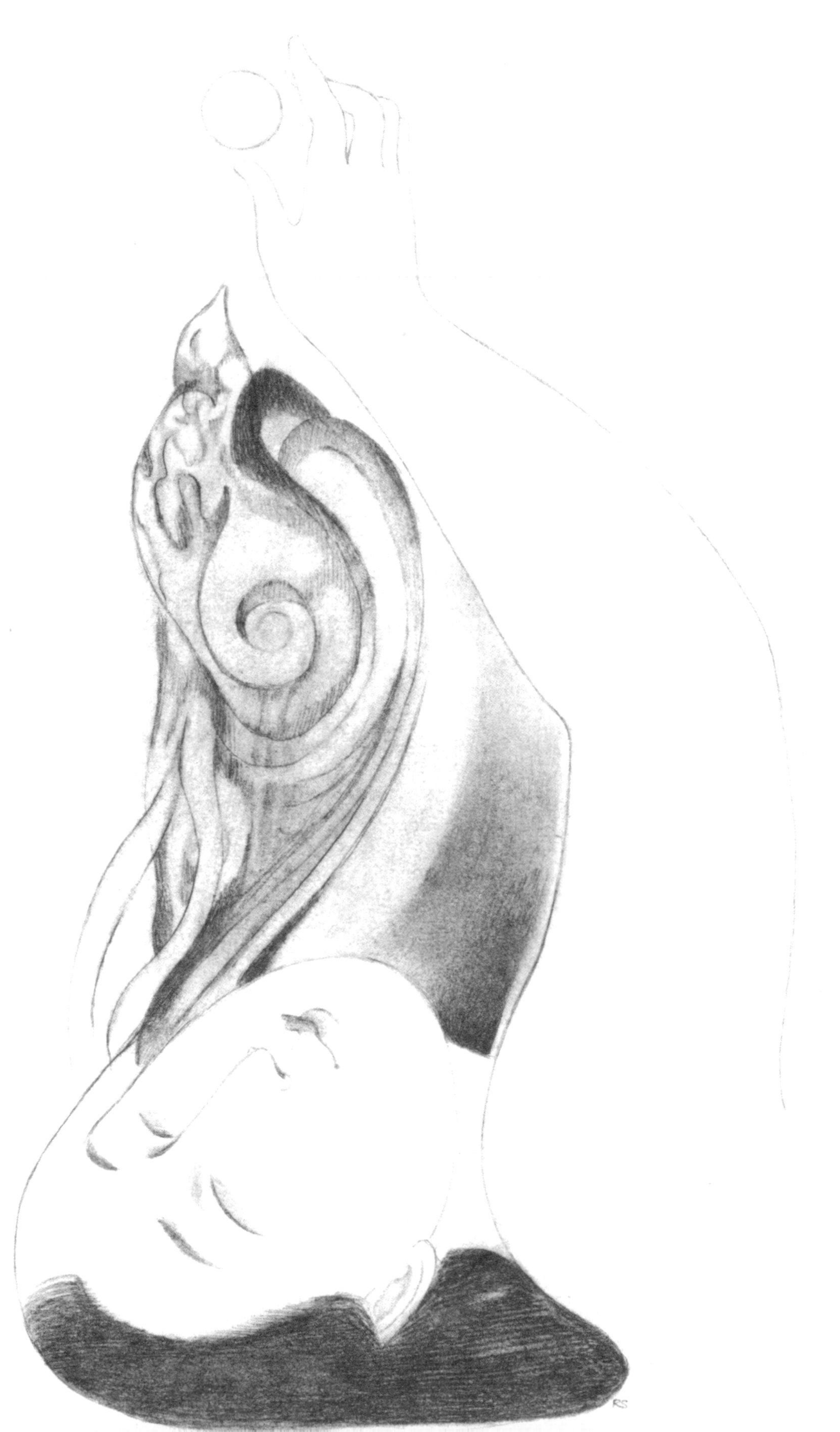

4 THE INNER GARDEN
Guided Imagery

Lie back
Let go
Begin to hear the waves
Feel the soft sand beneath you
the sun's rays above you
bathing each cell in warmth
the sea breezes caressing your skin
Let go...

The adventures of the mind
are immense
We can journey into richness and depth
beyond time and location
To enter into this adventure,
we allow
logic, reason, and comparison
to be neither guide nor excess baggage

In ceremony
we are able
to touch a deeper inner peace
Here we can expand
our intuitive awareness
Sensation and feeling
become alive
We taste a forgotten nectar

As the giver
you become a guide
Your words
soft in tone
slow in pace
lead your beloved into sanctuary

GUIDELINES

When you communicate instructions
or lead a guided imagery
be non-demanding
Never express judgment, anger, or impatience
through voice or actions
Laughter as a shared joy, however, is a delight
Let your voice
be soft and gentle
almost as if lullabying an infant

To begin
invite the recipient
to remove her shoes
and to loosen tight clothing
Alternatively
she might be in a robe or nude
Contact lenses may require removal

Next assist her to sit or lie down comfortably
Be certain that she feels warm
as the body generates little heat
in a guided imagery

Now suggest that she close her eyes
and bring her awareness
to her breath
taking a few fuller inhalations
Perhaps give a laying on of hands
on her abdomen and forehead

After about five minutes of these relaxation inductions
she will likely be ready
for an inner journey

Your *imagery introduction* might be like this:

> Now I am going to invite you to imagine an event. Whatever comes into your awareness is perfect, even if it does not fit my words. There are no right or wrong experiences. Allow whatever comes up to come up. While I may say "imagine" or "visualize," be open to feeling, sensing, intuiting, and any other means of perception available to you. If you are not aware of a response, allow that to be OK. Be open to experiencing any feeling or sensation in your body.

Now explore the following inner journey
(Perhaps make the guided imagery
a ceremony in itself)
Present the wording
as your own creation
rather than simply reading it
(A "..." means to take a longer pause
perhaps about ten seconds)
There is no need to be dramatic
Yet, allow feeling in the delivery

The recipient
may become very deeply relaxed
She may even appear to be asleep
Do not worry
Most likely she is soaring
Simply continue guiding the imagery
If she should be asleep
know that she is receiving a needed rest

THE EARTH COMMUNION IMAGERY

Here we give thanks
to the beauty and nourishment
our planet provides
Begin with the relaxation inductions and imagery introduction
Perhaps be aware
of your own inner images as you speak

> I'd like you to begin to imagine yourself walking down a path in a forest. Let it be an imaginary forest. It is a beautiful and serene place...

Earth Communion Imagery

Now begin to be aware of how your feet feel as you walk down the path. You may have on boots or shoes. Perhaps you are wearing sandals, or maybe you're barefoot. Feel the texture, the softness or the hardness of the earth each time your foot touches the ground. Notice if the path is narrow or wide. Notice if it is rocky or maybe muddy. Hear the sound of your footsteps. Let this be very real for you. Whatever feelings you have are fine. This forest is a special place. There is a richness and a beauty here. Allow your senses to perceive and to enjoy...

As you walk down this path begin to notice the trees around you. As the sunlight comes through the trees, see the shadows. Also, notice the subtle changes in the forest colors. Look all around you and perceive all the varying shapes...

Smell all the wonderful fragrances that the breezes bring. There are some places where the sun is more intense and you can smell the warmth. The places in the shade may have a different fragrance. There's a world of many subtle smells along this path. Allow yourself to experience them...

From time to time you may hear birds sing and other sounds of the forest. Maybe you can hear the trees creaking as the winds swish through their branches. You might even hear small animals scurrying through the brush...

Be open to feeling peaceful on this path. Allow yourself to be with each step, each vision, each fragrance. To commune with nature is precious. Allow yourself this...

Walking down the path, you'll find there is a clearing off to the side, maybe like a meadow, where it is soft and very easy to rest. When you see this clearing, walk over to it. As you enter, you can even smell the warmth of the sun. Find a comfortable place to lie down there. Notice how easy it is to totally let go and to allow all your muscles to relax. Feel yourself being supported by the earth beneath you. There is nothing to do except to let go...

As you rest there, begin to become aware of the warmth of the sun that comes to touch your skin. Even through your clothing you can feel the warmth. The rays penetrate each cell of your body. You can feel a gentle tingling as the cells are bathed in the

Earth Communion Imagery

sun's energy. Feel it penetrating all the way to the core of your body, nurturing you. Allow yourself to melt into the earth...

Let's take a moment to give thanks. To give thanks to life. To give thanks to the beauty of Earth. To give thanks to the warmth of the sun. To give thanks to the breezes and the fragrances they bring. To give thanks for the abundance of food. To give thanks for the water. This is a special place where we live. All we have to do is to open ourselves to perceive and enjoy these abundant gifts. With your inner voice take a moment to give thanks to this planet...

OK. Let's begin to come back now. Know that these images and feelings are available to you anytime you wish. Begin to take some fuller breaths. Perhaps inhale and hold your breath a couple of seconds before letting go... Begin to feel your body as it rests here on the bed (carpet, etc.). Come back even more. And when you feel ready, open your eyes and share your experiences with me.

(If this guided imagery is the beginning of a longer ceremony, perhaps the verbal sharing would be better after the whole ceremony.)

When she returns
    be present
    be close

This is one of many possible inner journeys
    Create your own if you wish
        Use memories or make-believe
        Visit the future
        Visit the past
            different cultures
            different lifetimes
    Explore one of these scenes:
        sitting on a secluded beach
        listening to a babbling brook
        drifting on a raft down a lazy river
        soaring on the back of a large silver-white bird

5 SENSUAL COMMUNION
Feeding

Smell
Taste
Savor
Slow down
Feel
Let the moment last
Linger in the energy

WHAT TO FEED

Is there food or drink
the recipient dislikes or excludes from her diet?
Any allergies?
Ask her if you do not know
Ask a friend if you wish to surprise
Perhaps serve the following suggestions
Perhaps be adventurous

Sparkling Nectars or Other Beverages

Sparkling apple cider or sparkling grape juice
often are first choices
Usually one bottle is sufficient

Fruit juices, especially very cold apple juice,
or a multiple-fruit purée
titillate tastes as well
If you prefer champagne
select a very dry or brut variety
Wine is probably better accompanying meals

Fruits

These are some favorites
mangoes, papayas, kiwis
strawberries, bananas
apples (a sweet variety such as Red or Golden Delicious)
persimmons, fresh berries
grapes (preferably seedless)
watermelon, nectarines, peaches
plums, cherries
Other possibilities are
pears, cantaloupes and other melons
coconuts, pomegranates
oranges, grapefruits, pineapples
Though be cautious
mixing citrus or other acid-tasting fruits
with whipped cream and nuts
Usually you need purchase only
one piece of each fruit
except for the berries, grapes, and strawberries
Variety is the key
There are seasonal variations and
markets vary in quality

Nuts

Nuts provide a crunchy, chewy contrast
to fruit and whipped cream
Perhaps serve a single variety of nut
that enhances rather than dominates other flavors
Almonds are an excellent choice
Other selections might be walnuts or pecans

Whipped Cream

The texture and the taste of whipped cream
either hand-whipped or electric-beater-whipped
can be incredible

A half pint or pint of the thickest cream is plenty
Save *prewhipped* whipped cream for a last resort
Use whipped cream substitutes
only when dietary restrictions necessitate

Alternatively, prepare a fruit sauce
of honey or maple syrup
with a half or whole pint of plain sour cream
or plain yogurt

Other Possibilities

The following
are not likely to be favorites
but you can explore them

In general, a mild cheese
is more likely to blend
than a sharp variety
Fruit-flavored cheeses are often very interesting
Do not overdo the cheese and crackers
— a heavy stomach in a sensual ceremony
would be a distraction

Candies,
such as extra fine chocolate,
and baked desserts
might be all right
but only in very small amounts
and only when especially desired
Candies have a tendency
to overwhelm the taste buds
and baked desserts may be too filling

Given an emphasis on fruit,
hors d'oeuvres or any salty or tart delight
might clash
When uncertain
try them yourself before the ceremony

Some tantric sexual rituals
use grains and meats
You can experiment with these
after becoming familiar with the preceding suggestions

Preparation and Arrangement

PREPARATION AND ARRANGEMENT

To have fully ripened fruit
you may need to shop a few days before your ceremony
Canned, frozen, or unnecessarily processed ingredients
are only as a last resort

To prepare and arrange the ceremonial platter
anticipate at least an hour
While the recipient will see the design
on the ceremonial platter for a few minutes only,
her memory may last for a lifetime

You may need the following
- a platter: a little larger than a standard dining plate
  perhaps of clear glass or stainless steel
- a cutting board and a knife for the fruit
- a serving spoon
- utensils for preparing the whipped cream or sauce
- one or two champagne glasses
  perhaps a tulip shaped wine glass
  rather than the standard champagne glass

For the first step
make the sparkling nectar
(a sparkling cider/juice or champagne)
very cold
If the ceremony location is a hotel or motel
have the beverage very cold before leaving home
since some ice buckets have only a chilling effect
If possible, chill the glasses

Next prepare the whipped cream
Hand whisking requires extensive energy
but the texture is sometimes finer
than that from an electric beater
The whipping is often easier
if the mixing bowl and whipping cream are cold
During the whipping
add about two teaspoons of sugar
and perhaps a little vanilla
Real maple syrup is another possible sweetener
added according to taste
though some find the flavor too strong
Be careful not to whip too long
as you might produce butter
If you are going to take the whipped cream to another location
you can put it in a plastic container with a lid

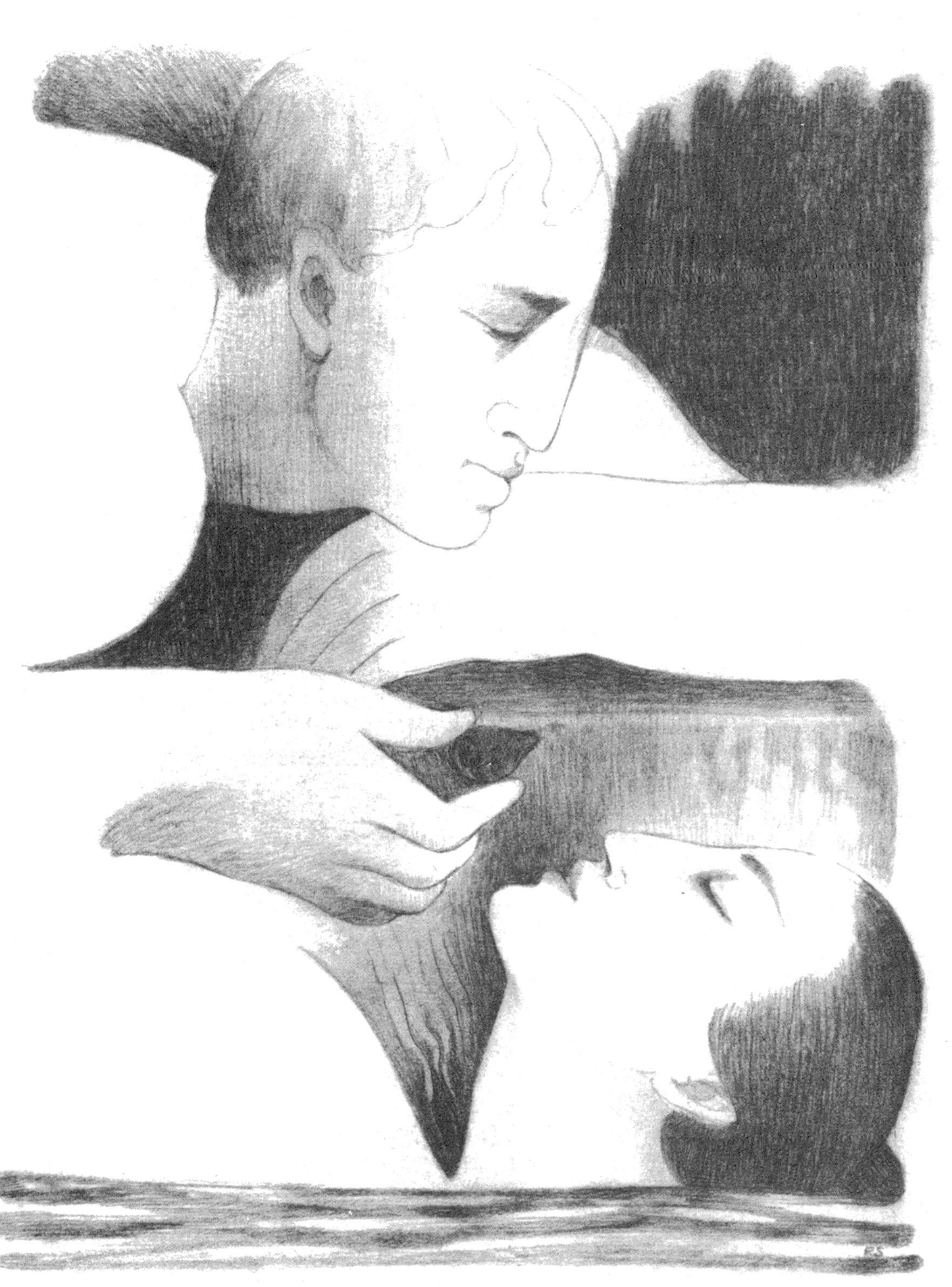

Preparation and Arrangement

To prepare a fruit sauce
of honey or maple syrup with sour cream or yogurt,
heat the honey or maple syrup
until it almost begins to simmer
Then pour and mix it
into the sour cream or yogurt
Continue tasting until lightly sweetened

Some suggestions for preparing the fruits
First, wash thoroughly
and taste each fruit for texture and ripeness
Purchasing a wide variety of fruits
ensures quality

- kiwi
  cut off the ends, and quarter lengthwise, with skin on
- papaya
  cut in half lengthwise and scoop out all the seeds
- mango
  cut lengthwise along each side of the large seed
  On each of the two serving sections
  make horizontal and vertical slices
  (in the meat, not the skin)
  and then curl the section inside out
- persimmon
  slice the skin from the tipped point
  (like petals of a flower)
  and gently fold back the slices
- grapes
  leave clustered on the branch
- strawberries
  perhaps leave the stems on until serving
- apple and pear
  quarter and slice vertically into thin slices
  Slice just before presenting
  or sprinkle lime or lemon juice on the slices
- banana
  slice into small cross sections

The arrangement
depends on which fresh fruits are available
as well as the size and shape of the serving platter
Here are some possibilities
Line the banana slices
on the outer rim of the platter
Then on each slice
place a single almond
systematically pointing in some direction
Apple slices could also line the outer rim

Fill the papaya with whipped cream
and a strawberry or cherry on top
A champagne glass is an alternative to the papaya
Use the different colors of the fruits in the design

Never let the recipient see the preparation process
Upon completion
cover and hide the platter
so that she does not have a sneak preview
and the cat does not get into the whipped cream
Keeping the preparation in the refrigerator, though,
may over-chill the fruit

A few extra pointers
when the ceremony is given in a hotel or motel room
Order ice and an ice bucket
a good while before the ceremony
In most hotels you can also order
a spoon, glasses, and a platter or large plate
A good cutting knife may not be available to guests
If room service hesitates about delivering
without a food or drink purchase,
offer to pay for the usage
One final touch,
if you are using a tray, you can also place on it
a small vase with a single flower

FEEDING CEREMONIES

While you are making the final touches
the recipient can be relaxing
listening to quiet music
Or she could be by the fireplace
sipping hot tea
Hearing the nearby sounds of food preparation
may build suspense
if she can not see the activity
Soften the lights if possible
Unplug the telephone
eliminate other possible interruptions
And do not burn incense
too soon before the actual feeding

A feeding ceremony
can be in combination with a bathing
as in a Secret Garden Ceremony

or it can be a ceremony in itself
Here are some guidelines
common to both situations

Present the platter for a visual feast
Let it say
"This is just for you"
Then ask if there is anything there
that she wishes not to eat
After setting the platter down
ask if she would like
to be surprised
or to request
If "to be surprised" is the response
invite her to close her eyes
If the mood shifts to requesting
flow with it
When feeding
slowly place the selection just in front of her lips
so that she can smell the aromas
If she is not aware of the presence
very lightly touch the food to her lips
This feeding is not intended
as a guessing game about what is served
Now is a time for her to be in the direct experience
of taste and smell
rather than discussing the topic
Gently encourage focusing on the sensations
Feed with your fingers
An inch above her tongue
squeeze grapes, strawberries, or watermelon
and let the sweet juices drop
drip by drip
When serving
vary the flavors and textures
Explore combinations
Feed slowly
Wait until she has thoroughly savored
the previous serving
If you should wish to taste also
first ask permission to serve yourself
Should she want to feed you
remind her that this is a time
for her to be served
She can give that as a gift another time
Exceptions are always negotiable
At some point let her know that she is to indicate
when she is satiated

THE EPICUREAN BATH

This is a very special, unique gift
It is simply the combination
of feeding and bathing in a bath
Certain exquisite experiences
are far more accessible *in* a bath
than outside of a bath
Before giving an epicurean bath
become familiar with the ceremonial bathing
in the next chapter

After you escort the recipient to the bath
perhaps leave momentarily
to give her an opportunity
to adjust to the womb-like environment
When you return
you can be nude
carrying the platter of delights,
the sparkling nectar, a glass, and a spoon
Immediately but without rushing
present the platter for her visual feast

Serve the sparkling nectar or other beverage first
If it is champagne
place a cloth over the cork
and pointing it away from her and yourself
slowly twist or rock the cork back and forth
until it gently pops
Pour the sparkling nectar into the glass
Without rushing
place the sparkling bubbles under her nose
to be inhaled
If she reaches up as if to serve herself
remove the glass to say non-verbally
"Please allow yourself to be served"
Usually by the second or third removal
your communication is clear

Cup Runneth Over

After a while
there is a special way
to serve a sparkling nectar
Perhaps warn the recipient by asking
"Are you ready for something delightfully different?"
As she is sipping

allow the sparkling nectar
to run over onto her chin and chest
Her first response may be
shock at the temperature
If she is appalled by the *waste*
this is the perfect time
to lavish even more upon her body
Also be sensitive to the possibility
that she may find the sensations undesirable
and be prepared to stop

Sparkling Shower

If she especially enjoys the sparkling thrills above
invite her to stand
Step into the tub and embrace her
Then pour directly from the bottle
so that the bubbles slither down
between your chests, abdomens, and pelvises
Hopefully there is something to lean against
— it may be difficult to stand up at this point
After a while invite her to resume sitting
and continue the feeding

Sparkling Kiss

Take a sip of sparkling nectar
and while kissing her
allow it to flow from your lips

Sparkling Massage

Take a large sip of sparkling nectar without swallowing
Then place your mouth
on her neck, breasts, fingers, toes, or elsewhere
and give an oral massage
as the sparkling essence seeps through your lips

Palm Sundae

An advantage to feeding in the bath
is that if anything slips from your hands or her lips
the experience can be a part of the ceremony

Place whipped cream and several fruits
such as banana, mango, papaya, and strawberries
in your palm
With the edge of the spoon
make a sort of purée
Next, place your closed palm against her lips
Squeeze
and slowly ooze the lusciousness
through her lips

Creaming and Papaya Pleasure

Wait until she feels sufficiently fed
before beginning these next treats
She may be uninterested in eating more afterward
For Creaming
abundantly stroke whipped cream
over her chest, abdomen, arms, and legs
She may wish then
that you taste your creamed creation
Creaming with the sour cream and honey sauce
is too sticky for most people
Here as always
avoid sugared ingredients in the vaginal area
as this might lead to yeast difficulties

Follow with Papaya Pleasure
or Persimmon Pleasure, or Mango Pleasure
As with the cream
slide the fruit all over her body
With the persimmon
first remove the seed if necessary
With the papaya and mango
shape the fruit so that the soft, fleshy meat
comes fully in contact with her skin
Sometimes in Creaming or Papaya Pleasure
the recipient goes into a partial trance
Do not worry
Following this
pour water on her for several minutes
Now bathe with soap and water
as described in the next chapter

FEEDING OUTSIDE THE BATH

There are other locations for a feeding ceremony,
the floor, the bed, or any comfortable place in nature
Here the recipient's position
is lying down on her back
This body position and non-bath setting
usually create a quite different mood
than in the Epicurean Bath

Invite the recipient to lie down
with her head in your lap
She can lie so that you face her feet
or she can be perpendicular to you
Perhaps place a pillow under her head
as well as underneath yourself
This position necessitates chewing
rather than gulping the food
However, since drinking
is very difficult in this position
provide plenty of juicy fruit
(A possible option
would be to provide a straw that bends
or a wine-carrying pouch with a spout)

Between each feeding
stroke her hair and brow
These caresses help relax her even more
In general, the greater the relaxation
the more pleasurable the tastes
From time to time
use a napkin or damp cloth
to very gently wipe off excesses
from her chin and cheeks
When she is full
continue stroking for a while
perhaps with a facial massage

At the end of the ceremony
she may feel very relaxed and nurtured

Rest

Cuddle

Feel

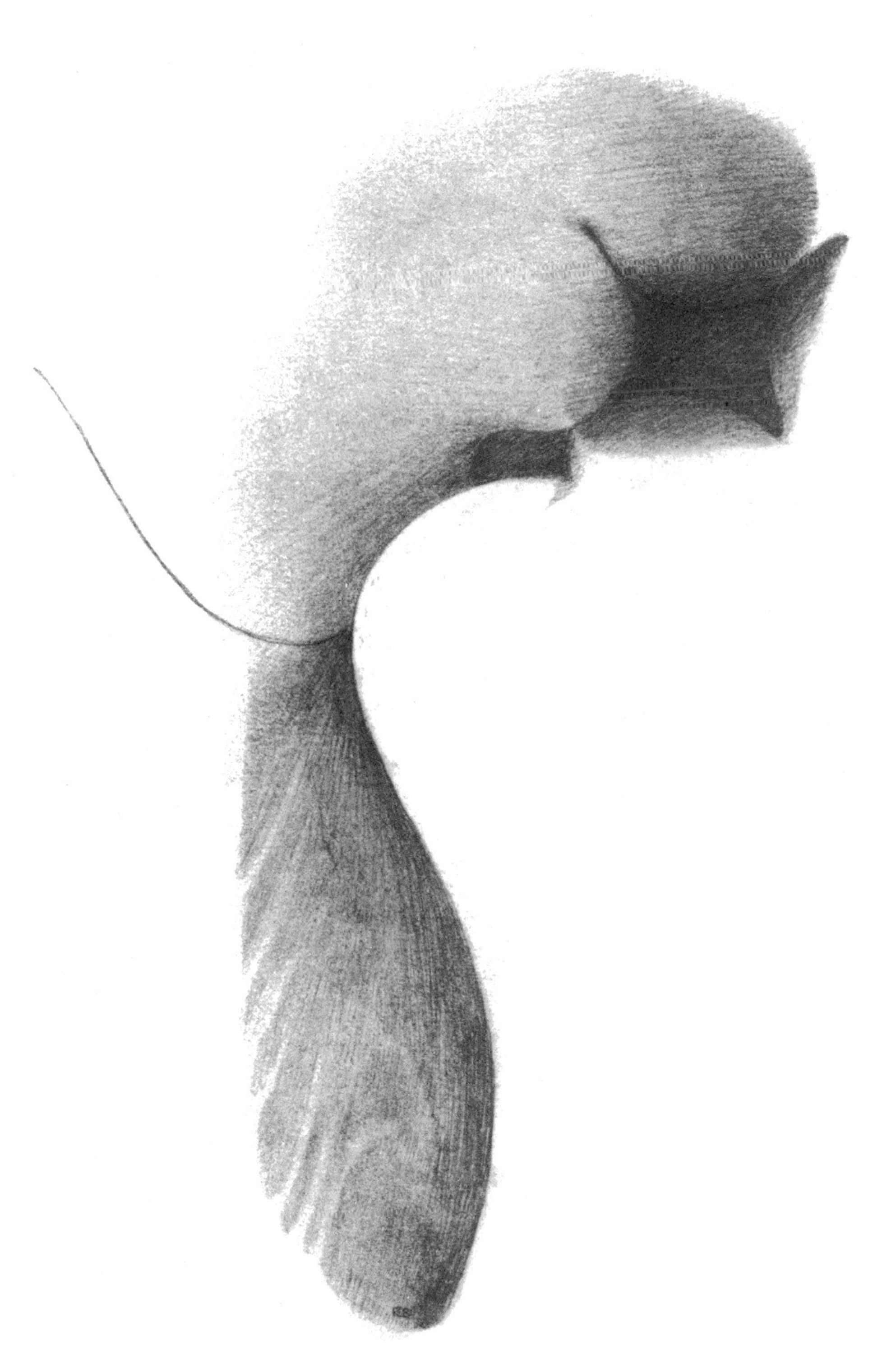

6 CEREMONIAL WATERS
Body and Foot Bathing

Soft
Warm
Soothing
Boundless
Enter into the ceremonial waters

A pool or stream in nature
a bathtub
a basin
a shower
a hot tub
Ceremonial waters abound

In a Secret Garden Ceremony
a bathtub is usually the location of choice
There is privacy and no insect intrusions
the recipient can recline
the water temperature is easily adjustable

For a shorter ceremony
a foot bathing is especially nurturing
Also, it can be easily given
to someone who is not a sexual partner

BODY BATHING

If you are giving a bathtub bath,
a home or hotel/motel
are the most likely environments
At home you have many comforts
but may need to make extensive rearrangements
to the ceremonial bathing area
When making a reservation at a hotel or motel
confirm that the bath is not only a shower stall

Accessories

There are several essentials
hot water
soap
towels
and something for pouring water

Liquid soap with peppermint or almond essence
are many people's preference
Purchase them at health food or natural food stores

Select a towel to cover a cold tile floor
if the bath mat is missing
You may need a washcloth for cooling the recipient's brow
For drying
reserve at least three bath towels
And if you are including feeding
a small towel may be necessary for your hands
In most hotels you will have to order additional towels

For pouring water
use either a container, or a natural sponge, or both
An ideal pouring container in a bathtub
is plastic
and about a foot long and four inches in diameter
Larger or bulky containers
may make water dipping very difficult
And glass containers are elegant but breakable

Other nice accessories are
a candle, loofas, a bath brush
fragrances for the bath water
maybe bubble bath or bath salt ingredients

a bath pillow, possibly a rubber stopper
plants, and music

A candle is almost a necessity
Its flame transforms
Place the candle
either at the foot of the tub
or in front of a mirror

Loofas are the thick fibrous interiors of a type of fruit
When they are wet
they create an exciting sensation on the skin
especially on the bottom of the feet
the buttocks, and the back
With a loofa mitt
(a loofa on one side
and a washcloth on the other)
you can have one on each hand

Natural-fiber bath brushes create an exotic sensation
similar to the loofa

Delicate fragrances arising from the bath
deepen the involvement of the senses
The fragrances might come from bath salts,
bath oils, or bubble bath added to the water
Prior to putting anything in the bath water
ask if the future recipient's skin is sensitive
to any ingredients
Also, be cautious of synthetic chemical scents and colors
that are in many products

One method of adding fragrances is
to put one or two drops (careful, not too much)
of essential oil of lemon, orange, spearmint,
or peppermint
into the stream of hot water
when the bath is almost full
Another way is to steep herbs enclosed in a cloth bag
as you begin drawing the bath

A bath pillow, purchased from a bath shop
comforts the recipient's neck and head
Rolled-up towels are a substitute
but have a tendency to slide into the water

Occasionally a bath drain plug
will not make a complete seal

Before using an unfamiliar tub
perhaps purchase a flat rubber disk
at a hardware store

Plants, if easily available, add ambiance

In a ceremonial bath
music with candle light creates an encompassing dome
separating you and your special friend
from the outside world
The selection of music, however, is a crucial step
to be taken before the day of the bath
Disco and rap music will probably not be in harmony
with the mood
In most cases
a portable cassette tape player is quite suitable

And if you wish
a rubber ducky

Preparations

These are the behind-the-scenes preparations
to eliminate potential distractions
and to add to the nuances

In a massage
the recipient's eyes are closed
In a bath
her eyes are often open
Here are some ways to nurture the visual sense as well

Remove the shower curtain
and if possible, the shower curtain bar
The sliding bath doors, however,
might be a real stumbling block
You may need a regular or Phillips screwdriver
With perseverance, ingenuity,
and sometimes brute force
most sliding doors will come off
If they just won't come off,
adapt the ceremony
by sliding the doors back and forth as needed
(You will want to place a rolled towel
between your buttocks and the metal tracks
on which the doors slide)

Body Bathing

If the tub itself does not appear or feel clean
bathe it
Be sure to rinse off all of the cleanser
— sandpaper is no fun
Even clean out the soap dish
and the upper corners of the tub

Next remove almost everything that is movable
in the bathing room
Start with the shampoo bottle
all the bars of soap
the toothpaste tops
the shaving utensils
the toilet brush
the wastepaper basket
almost everything
Remove reading materials from sight
Any towels not intended to be used
can be placed elsewhere
(Exceptions might be a decorative object
and the roll of toilet paper on the holder)

Most important,
remember everything's original location
as well as where you hide it
After the ceremony
you will put everything back in place

Here are some additions

Perhaps minimize outside light
If there are windows or a skylight
you might cover them with a towel or dark sheet
Though when the window is large and the view is beautiful
it may be best to leave it uncovered

Now the water
If you are not sure how much hot water is available
run a half tub of hot water
about a half hour before the beginning of the bath
Then just prior to the beginning
more hot water will likely be available
Test the water temperature with your foot or inner forearm
Be sure to check it again
just before inviting your guest into the bathing room
When the bath is almost full
is the best time to add fragrances, bath oils
or bubble bath
Herbs can be added at the beginning
since they usually need to steep

One more suggestion,
if the toilet is in the same room as the bath
use it before escorting in the recipient
There may not be an opportune moment
during the one- to two-hour ceremony

Now you are ready
for your guest of honor

THE BATHING CEREMONY

Beginning

Candle lit
water temperature tested
music on?

If you have a kimono
wear it to greet the recipient
who is in another room relaxing, possibly in a robe

Bow and announce to her
"Your bath is prepared"
Then escort her into the bathing room

Now you can either undress her
or invite her to disrobe
and sit in the bath while you momentarily leave
But before leaving
inform her how to adjust the hot and cold water
just in case
Leaving the room for a few minutes
allows her to use the toilet
and then settle into the warm bath water
the fragrances, and the candle light
You can disrobe before returning

Almost anything we do with soap and water
can easily create a ceremonial feeling
When you are ready to bathe
try the following sequence
Bathing is relatively free-form
However, you can use massage strokes as guidelines

Remember to have fun
Getting her clean
is not the objective here

Feet and legs

Begin with your feet in the water
and sitting on the tub rim near the recipient's feet
Gracefully lift one of her legs
to rest on your thigh,
the one nearest the foot end of the tub
After applying soap to your hands
spread it on the foot and leg
Use soap abundantly
Move slowly, attentively
After using varying movements and pressures
for several minutes,
stroke the bottom of the foot with a loofa
if one is available
(Make sure the loofa has softened
by soaking it a few seconds first)
Perhaps using a sponge
now pour water over her leg and foot
There is no need, however,
to restrict the pouring to just the soapy areas

When the first leg is completed
gently lower it back into the bath
and raise the other leg onto your thigh
Repeat the lathering, stroking, and water pouring

Arms and Hands

Slide up the tub rim to reach the arms

A hint,
if the receiver is shorter than the bathtub
there is a tendency
for her to slide down towards the foot end
The solution is to place your foot
(the one nearest the foot end of the tub)
between her legs
so that her pelvic floor rests against your ankle
This gentle pressure on the pelvis often feels comforting

Once established
lather, stroke, and rinse one arm and hand
and then the other
For some, a loofa is too rough here

Front Torso

Now bathe the abdomen, chest, and breast areas
For the portion of the body underneath water
apply even more soap

On the abdomen
make circular movements
This is also a good position
from which to bathe the pelvic area
Be careful using peppermint soap
if you include
the vaginal or anal membranous tissue areas
— the mentholated effect might be too much

If the bath water has cooled
add more hot water
evenly distributing it by stirring
With the chest exposed to the cooler air
it is particularly nice to pour water there
The warmth and soft flow on the heart
are very nurturing

Hair Washing

If the recipient wishes
you can wash her hair
either before or after washing her back
However, it seems in most situations
the hair washing is best given as a ceremony
in itself
After an extensive bath
the mood is usually more conducive
to lying down, resting, perhaps cuddling
than drying and brushing
Experiment for yourself
Whenever you give a hair washing
use plenty of lather
And when pouring water
check with her regarding the water temperature

If the hair is washed during a body bath
remember to rinse with fresh water

Back

Sitting in the tub to give the back bathing
is wonderfully cozy
If it is desirable and possible to get into the tub
invite her to sit up slowly
and slide forward a few feet
Then cuddle in from behind
with your legs spread to each side
While she is leaning forward
with her head relaxed downward
lather up the back

Extra attention
to the upper back and shoulders
is special
Sliding your thumbs down along the grooves
just to each side of the spine is likewise

Two loofas mitts can double the pleasure
Be firm sliding them downward on each side of the spine
though too many passes can be irritating

Now with the container
pour water over the back
for a minute or two

Conclusion of Bathing

Invite her to lean back slowly
onto your chest
Continue pouring the water
for several more minutes
Pouring from this position
can be a little awkward
but it is worth it
Remember, there is no rush

Once you've completed the pouring
simply hold her
perhaps with one of your hands resting on her abdomen
and the other hand over her heart

Then most importantly
follow her breath
and breathe in unison:
Inhale as she inhales
exhale as she exhales

Breathe like this for maybe five or ten minutes
Perhaps by then
time will have disappeared

Drying Off

When it comes time to leave the bath
ask her to lean forward
and remain there while you get up
and prepare for the drying

Once you are ready
suggest that she rise S L O W L Y
Assist with your hands
— it may not be easy to stand up
and step out of a tub after a bath like this

Now begin the drying
On the upper part of the body
wrap one towel from the back
and one from the front
If her hair is wet
take a separate towel to dry it a little
Next, with a combination
of patting
and sliding your hands up and down and in circles
over the towel surface,
dry her back, front torso, and arms
If the towels do not reach down to her hands
use a separate towel

Leaving the towels on the upper portion of the body
dry one leg at a time
with the up and down and circular motions
over the towel surface
Make sure the inner thighs, genitals, and inner buttocks
are dried
With a fresh towel
gently pat dry her face and neck

Ask if anywhere still feels damp

Next ask if she wishes to lie down
On a bed or in front of a fireplace
may be options
If you are planning to give a massage
direct her to the massage location

To assist in the transition
out of this etheric bathing womb,
inform her before opening the door
that outside
the light may be brighter
and the air cooler

If you wish
you can present
the rubber ducky as a memento afterward

FOOT BATHING CEREMONY

If you want to give a gift
that is both relaxing and simple
a foot bathing is perfect
Of all the techniques presented in this book
the foot bathing
is the most widely applicable
to friends who are not sexual partners
Grandparents, bosses, employees, teachers
and many others
can be profoundly nurtured

What You Need

These are the basics
which may already be around the house
soap, perhaps liquid soap
a plastic basin
or any container large enough for at least one foot
at least three towels

Additionally there could be
a large, comfortable chair for the recipient
relaxing music in the background
and elimination of possible disruptions
such as the telephone

As the giver
you may want to sit on a pillow or cushion
to lessen any strain on your legs and hips

Initial Steps

Perhaps lower the lights
put on soothing music
light a candle
and do anything else to create a desirable ambiance

Then with your friend relaxing in a comfortable chair
lying on the carpet
or lying on a bed with her knees bending over the edge
draw the water in the basin
Usually the temperature is best
very warm bordering on hot
You can always add hot water later
after her feet have become accustomed to the heat
If, however, the weather outside is really hot
lukewarm or cool water may be preferable

Take off her shoes and socks
Since most people are not used
to having this done for them
you may have to use gentle, verbal persuasion
If there are stockings
she may have to remove them
Next you roll up pants legs or skirts
to about the knee

This is also a good time
to invite your friend to allow the eyes to close
first removing contact lenses if necessary

After placing a towel underneath her feet
slide the basin near them
Lift one of her legs
supporting it
at the bottom of the foot
and at the calf or underneath the knee
Actually what you are doing
is non-verbally communicating to her
to let go and to allow herself to be taken care of
Place your lower hand
so that it will enter the water first
in case the temperature is too hot

If there is space
place the second foot in the basin also

Important,
make sure that her toes are not jammed
into the end of the basin
and that the rim of the basin is not wedged into her calves

Sometimes it's nice to let your friend rest in solitude
with her feet soaking for a short while

Bathing The Feet

Begin the bathing
with a laying on of hands in the water
One hand is on the side of the foot
the other is on top
Close your eyes
and let your hands relax into the touch
and the warmth of the water

After a minute or so
lift the foot and leg
and bring it out of the water
to rest on the towel or your leg
With a little maneuvering
slide the basin out of the way
if the other foot is not in the basin
Keeping at least some physical contact with your friend
place some soap in your hands
and then lather the foot
maybe even half way up the calf

As in all soap-and-water bathing
almost any stroke feels exquisite
So it is very easy to make up strokes as you go
If you wish to follow a pattern
use foot massage strokes
Continue to use lavish amounts of soap
and enough water to keep the bubbles

You can bathe and massage one foot
easily for fifteen minutes
But neither rush nor prolong the ceremony
If you are totally involved
and connected with the bathing and your friend,
time is no longer a reality

Since the recipient is usually quite relaxed
by the time you begin stroking
there is little likelihood of any ticklishness
If, however, it does occur
stroke more slowly and more firmly
And if the ticklishness should still remain
discontinue the bathing
There are other possible nurturing ceremonies

When ready
return the foot to the basin
Rinse the calf and foot
by cupping and pouring water with one or both hands

At this point
you can either remove the foot and dry it
or if the basin contains both feet
leave the first foot in
while soaping and massaging the second
Adding some hot water (carefully!)
might be desirable now

Drying Off

Use a dry towel for the following

Encompassing the whole foot with the towel
move the hands over the towel like this:
up and down
back and forth
and in small circles
Sliding the towel over the skin can be an exciting contrast
but for many the sensation
is too rough for the mood

For the toes
there is a special treat
Slip a folded edge of a towel
in between a set of toes
Then slide it gently upward for several inches

After the toes
take this towel or preferably a separate dry towel
and snugly wrap the foot

Once you have wrapped both feet
place one hand on each foot

Gradually squeeze to a medium firmness
    and hold a short while
When you feel ready
    release very slowly
    — even slowly enough
        that your friend is not able to discern
            when your hands have actually left contact

Afterward, perhaps continue to sit in meditation
    or curl up to rest on the floor

When your friend returns to the verbal world
    be open to hearing and sharing tender feelings
        for each other

7 TEMPLE OF THE SPIRIT
Massage

Hands listening
to contours and moods
Hands dancing
suggesting to let go
to feel
Hands singing pleasures long forgotten

More important
than the techniques
is
your own personal expression

More important than
your own personal expression
is
the recipient's wishes

More important than
the recipient's wishes
is
your never forcing yourself

Yet
be open to discovering
new horizons

It's a delicate dance

THE MASSAGE

For an extensive massage
consult *Tantric Massage*
Volume I of THE SECRET GARDEN TRILOGY
For a simpler
though equally as nurturing massage,
explore the following strokes
adapting to individual variations and circumstances,
including strokes with which you are already familiar

Initially, a massage
may be mainly a practice of strokes
The learning time will vary
for each person
Be gentle with yourself
in coordinating your mind, nervous system, and muscles
into some very new patterns
The gift is worth the perseverance

The following strokes can be adapted
to a massage table
or to a floor or bed massage
There is, however, no necessity
to massage the whole body
every time you touch
A neck or foot massage just by itself
could be exactly what is needed

Regarding the degree of pressure
a massage in a sensual pleasuring ceremony
usually is one of long, flowing movements
with a gentle touch
A heavier pressure, athletic massage
might be desirable for other occasions
When in doubt about the pressure
lighter might be better
The recipient's preference, however,
is the best guide

Guidelines

There are three simple guidelines
for making touch ceremonially sensual

The Massage

First and foremost
be present
Letting go of expectations of the future
and comparisons with the past
be here now

Secondly, for most strokes
maintain full-hand contact
whenever possible
Allow the palms, fingers, and thumbs
to outline the contours

Thirdly, maintain a continuous flow
Movements blend together
each one enhancing the preceding
and preparing the next

Following these guidelines
will bring a special touch to your ceremony
Allowing your hands to move intuitively
you can open doors to inner peace

Here are a few reminders

If the sensation feels good to the recipient
you are doing it correctly
— regardless of what theory or instructions might direct

Vary the pressure, tempo, and rhythm
Repeating a stroke in the exact same way each time
becomes boring very quickly
to both the recipient and the giver

Glide on and off
To begin a touch
rather than plopping on,
glide on with a slow descent
in the direction that your hands will be moving
In coming off
continue the movement in a gradual ascent
Generally, minimize landings and take offs

If there are two of them
massage both
For example
stroking the left leg only and not the right
will leave the recipient feeling very unbalanced
However,
just the head or just the feet are fine

Minimize the talking
An important exception
is when the recipient needs to communicate
deep feelings

Become centered
Nervousness or excessive excitement
can distract
Tuning into and slowing your breath
you can quieten yourself
Being centered
you will experience more deeply
your own pleasure as well

Preparations

Where?

Anywhere
as long as distractions and interruptions are minimized
Inside or outside is fine
When outside
take precautions for insects and excessive sun
When inside
unplug the phone
If the ceremony is in a home
arrange for all household members, including children
not to interrupt

It is very important
to maintain a warm temperature
This may mean using a portable heater
or covering parts of the recipient's body
not being massaged at the moment

When?

Perhaps celebrate
a special time
Sometimes you can be spontaneous

For an extensive ceremony
setting aside a specific day or evening
is often more conducive

With What?

Basically all you need is oil
either in a plastic squeeze bottle or a bowl
a towel or two
and a comfortable spot for the recipient to lie down

If you anticipate using feathers
or other tactile stimulators
have them close at hand

Massage tables are great
and tabletops padded with foam or blankets are fine
Make sure the table is sturdy
Otherwise, a padded floor, a bed
or the ground covered with cloth
is quite suitable
The beach
is fantastic when the sand is not a nuisance

For the covering cloth
select a sheet or other cloth
that is OK to be oiled
Some fabrics are difficult to clean
and the oil smell may not wash out

When lying on her front side
the recipient may need
a covered foam pad or a couple of rolled towels
placed under the front of the ankles
When she is lying on her back
if there is strain in her lower back
place the same pad underneath the knees

If you select a large bed
it is advantageous to have the recipient's head
at a corner at the foot of the bed
while her feet are pointing diagonally
toward the opposite corner
This allows you better access
to both the right and left sides

Perhaps use music, candle light or colored lights
incense, scented oils, flowers

interior design of the room
or whatever creates a comfortable ambiance
However, you do not have to create
an extravagant environment
every time you wish to pleasure another
Sometimes the only preparations necessary
are to close the door
and turn down the lights

Before Beginning

Everything ready?
Oil, phone unplugged
temperature warm enough
recipient's contact lenses removed (if necessary)
your hands warmed

Before beginning
it is good to ask
if there are any injuries or tender places
And remember to ask
if anything would be particularly pleasing
Check for other possible relevancies
such as oil in hair or time limitations

Once the recipient lies down
invite her to take a few fuller breaths
and to close her eyes

THE STROKES

The following set of strokes
can be learned
with almost no practice
They can be combined and adapted
to almost any part of the body
Modify, use your intuition,
use other strokes
with which you are already familiar

Laying On Of Hands

Especially to begin, to end the massage

As an autumn leaf in slow motion
allow your hands to come to rest
on your beloved

Be present
Just BE

When you feel complete
perhaps a minute or so later
slowly
allow your hands to ascend
also in slow motion

Both hands on the forehead
Both hands on the feet
One hand on the abdomen, the other on the forehead
One on the sacrum, the other on the lower neck
More important than the location
is your presence

Chapter 9 presents more details
under *Laying On Of Hands*

Feathering

Alternating your hands
gracefully caress
the surface of the recipient's skin

Short strokes, long strokes
The pads of your fingertips
delicately touch
sharing subtle pleasures

Anointing With Oil

Apply the oil
to your hands first
With circular movements
warm the oil
as you spread the oil all around your hands

Now anoint your partner
using strokes similar
to the following Palm Pulling and Squeezing & Sliding

Apply the oil
to just the section you are about to massage
or if you are using a massage table,
to one whole side of the body

The Strokes

Palm Pulling

Especially for the sides of the torso and hips,
the inner and outer sides of the thighs

Reach across your partner
and applying full contact with your palms and fingers
firmly but gently
pull with a sliding motion
across the skin and muscles beneath
Be careful when reaching to begin each stroke
not to pinch the skin against the table/mattress beneath

Squeezing & Sliding

Especially for the arms and fingers,
the legs and the feet

Here your thumb is on one side
and your fingers are on the other side
of an appendage
Give a gentle squeeze
and slide down and off

On the arm, leg, or foot
alternate your hands
so there is a continuous contact:
As one hand lifts up to begin again
the other continues sliding

On the fingers
use only one hand
allowing your fingers to encircle the recipient's finger
and then slide off

Drumming

Especially for the back, buttocks, and backs of thighs

Rest your palm on the recipient
while the other, closed hand
drums a primordial beat
for several minutes or longer
on the back side of the flat hand
Vary the tempo and the rhythm

Circling

Especially for the face

Applying a light pressure
with the flat pads of your thumb
or the flat pads of your fingers held closely together,
make circular movements

Most of the touch is with enough pressure
to slide the recipient's skin
over the muscles beneath

At the end of the massage
allow your beloved
to remain in bliss
After a few minutes
being very careful not to disturb or intrude
perhaps cuddle up beside

If it is suiting
tuck your ceremonial guest into bed
and read a bedtime story
to complete The Secret Garden Ceremony

Perhaps then with Spoon Breathing (see Chapter 9)
drift into astral-land

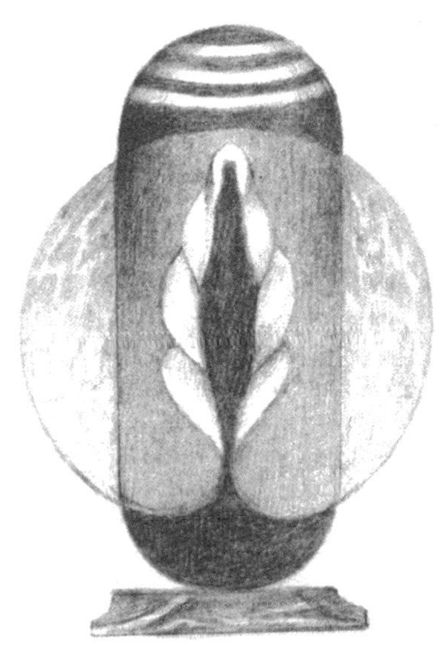

TANTRIC EXPLORATIONS

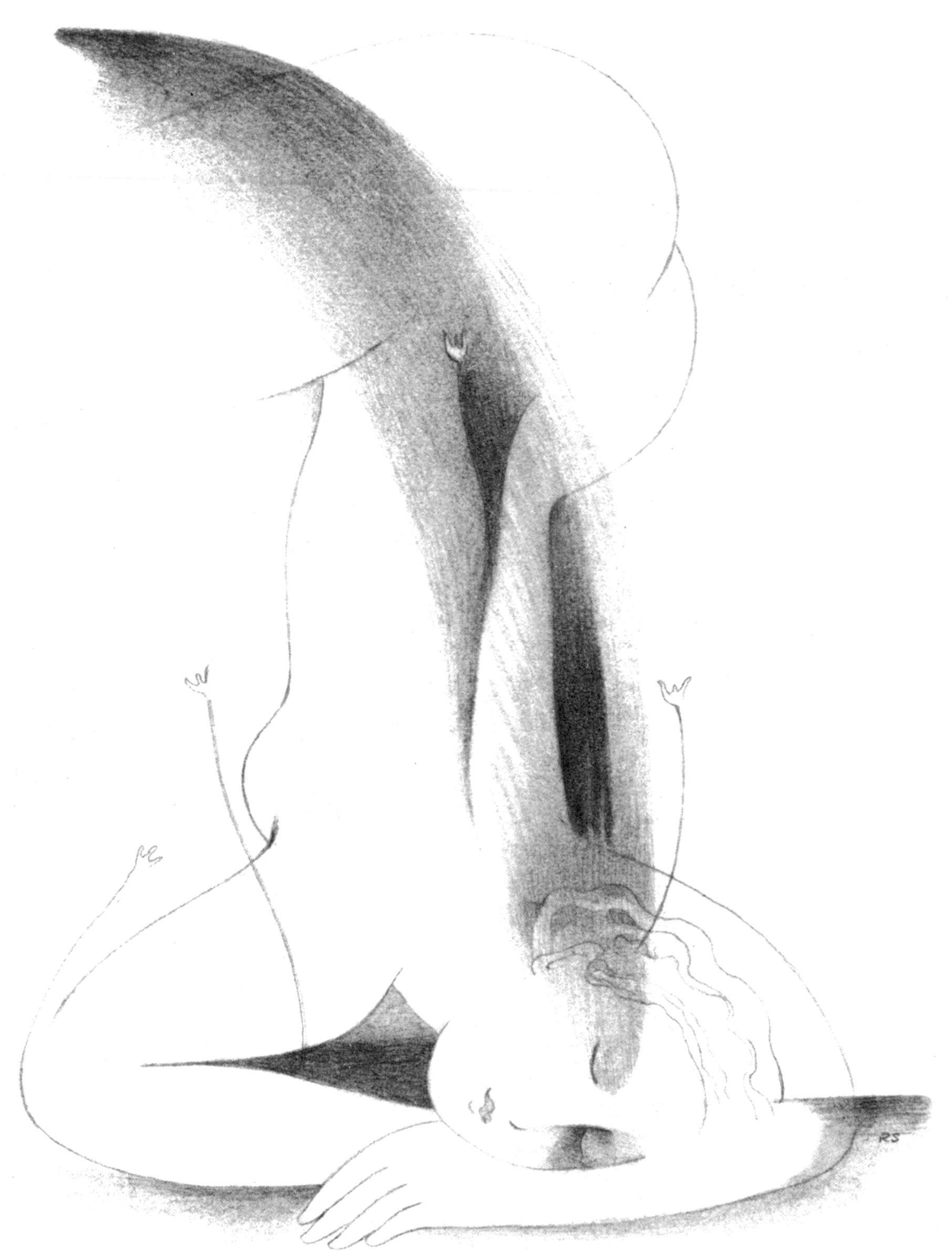

8 EQUANIMITY
Solo Meditations

Self-nurturing
is a gift of pleasure to ourself
This is where
sensuality, sexuality, and spirituality begin
— with ourself

An inner peace comes from realizing
that we already have it all within us
that it is possible to soar by ourself
Then when we are
with another out of a want to share
rather than out of a need to possess or control
there will be no strings of attachment
to bind and restrain

The following meditations/exercises/processes
are valuable for developing
a deeper appreciation of our senses
The focus is on relaxation
on stimulation of subtle energies
and on connection with our sensations/feelings

What is gained
enriches how we express our love to another
— in a sensual ceremony
and in daily life

Explore and feel

THE BREATH

The breath is essential to life
and to the celebration of life
Play with these breathing meditations
Find which are most suitable
for your individual inclinations

The Equal Breath

For some the Equal Breath is one of the simplest and most effective ways to create relaxation. You can either be sitting or lying down anywhere. It requires only about ten minutes of having not to place your attention on anything in particular.

First find a beat that will function as a metronome. Close your eyes and turn inward to find the heart beat sensation. If that is not perceptible, look for any pulsation in your body. And if you find none count an even beat in your mind.

Next measure the duration of your inhalation and exhalation by counting the number of beats in each. Usually, though not always, the inhalation and exhalation will be of different durations.

Now modify your breathing pattern to equalize the number of beats of the inhalation and the exhalation. The length of the two sets is not important as long as they are equal. If there is any discomfort, you might lengthen or shorten both sets.

Continue the Equal Breath meditation for about ten or more minutes. Five or less minutes may not be long enough to be beneficial. (If necessary set an alarm rather than watching a clock).

A Variation

Continuing with the Equal Breath, gradually lengthen the duration of both sets of beats. Once you have settled into a comfortable baseline equalization, you can add two beats to both the inhalation and the exhalation. After a few minutes, add two more beats. If there is any feeling of strain, simply subtract two beats, still maintaining the equal duration. As you feel ready, continue increasing the duration by two beats about two or three more times.

Both the Equal Breath and its variation are excellent for calming yourself in a stressful situation. They are unobtrusive and can thus be practiced easily even in public.

Ocean Breath

This is an extremely powerful breathing pattern. It is wonderful for massaging the abdominal organs and often places us in a very deep state of relaxation. This exercise will require lying down approximately twenty to thirty minutes without interruptions. If the air is chilly, you might want to cover yourself before beginning.

This is a double series of twenty-one breaths. In the first series, start with an easy, normal breathing. Make each succeeding inhalation fuller than the previous one. By the twenty-first inhalation you are at your maximum inhalation.

On the second series of twenty-one, reverse the pattern. Starting with the maximum inhalation, make each succeeding inhalation less full than the preceding one until you are back to your easy breathing by the twenty-first.

As you go along, you will be approximating each increasing or decreasing increment of inhalation. Adjust in progress as necessary. If you lose your count, simply estimate.

This pattern is named the *ocean* breath since the inhalation looks like an ocean wave rolling in: It fills up first at the pelvic floor and rolls up the abdomen, up the chest, and on up to the neck. In the first few breaths, however, the ocean-like movement will not be obvious.

To exhale, simply let go and let the breath flow or rush out on its own. Do not contract the chest or abdominal muscles.

To make certain the inhalation expands in both the lower abdomen and the chest, you can rest a palm on each area.

It is very, very important not to rush any of the breaths. When your body has plenty of oxygen, it may be several seconds after an exhalation before you feel any inclination to inhale again. Allow that pause. Here lies one of the secrets to experiencing a very sensuous pleasure: Allow yourself to sink deeply into the subtle vibrations of the pause. Like a humming bird tasting the nectar of a flower, in the stillness of the pause, place your attention into your inner sensations and enjoy.

After the double series of twenty-one breaths, lie quietly and immerse yourself in the wonderful energies you have generated. This would be an excellent time for Expanding Sensations, a meditation which follows shortly.

Initially, perhaps try this exercise once a day for three or four days to get a feel for it. Then use it whenever you wish.

Heart-to-Hand Breath

This meditation is for energizing your hands and sensitizing them to tactile stimulation. You accomplish this by combining your breathing with a visualization.

Sitting or standing with your eyes closed, bring your hands up to about the height of your heart with the palms facing each other and about six inches apart. Your elbows are at your sides and your shoulders are relaxed. It is important that you are relaxed in this position. The breathing is easy and normal though it is fine if it is fuller than usual.

Now combine the breathing with this visualization: When you inhale, imagine the breath coming into your heart center from all directions — above, below, from in front, from behind, from the sides. Then with the exhalation, imagine the breath flowing outward from the heart through the shoulders, through the arms and out the hands.

Repeat this twenty-five to fifty times. The more the repetitions, the more energy you may generate.

You can use the Heart-To-Hand Breath before a laying on of hands, a massage, and specifically the following Energy Sensing.

ENERGY SENSING

Immediately following a Heart-to-Hand Breath, explore the energy field surrounding the body. Here the hands are very sensitive sensing devices.

With your eyes closed, very slowly separate and move your palms back and forth toward each other about an inch. They are not to touch yet. You might imagine your hands as tall grass near the ocean, the breezes gently swaying them back and forth.

Now bring your hands to a stillness, move them together about an inch, and come to a stillness again.

Next very slowly move one hand up, while the other moves down. Then reverse and continue. As your palms move past each other, tune into any sensations of magnetic pulling together or pushing apart. Again bring the hands to a stillness, move them together another inch or so, and come to a stillness again.

Now move them around each other. Continue to be open to sensing warmth and coolness, pushing and pulling tendencies, and other tinglings or hummings in or around the hands. Still avoid any physical touching. Since your eyes are closed, however, the hands might touch occasionally. Once more bring the hands to a stillness with palm facing palm.

Now very, very slowly move your palms together. Experience not knowing when your hands will touch. Be aware of the moment before they touch, the moment that they touch, and the moment after they touch.

Then very gracefully let the hands stroke each other.

After a minute or so, gently caress your face. Notice the delicate sensations.

Be open to any appreciation of your body.

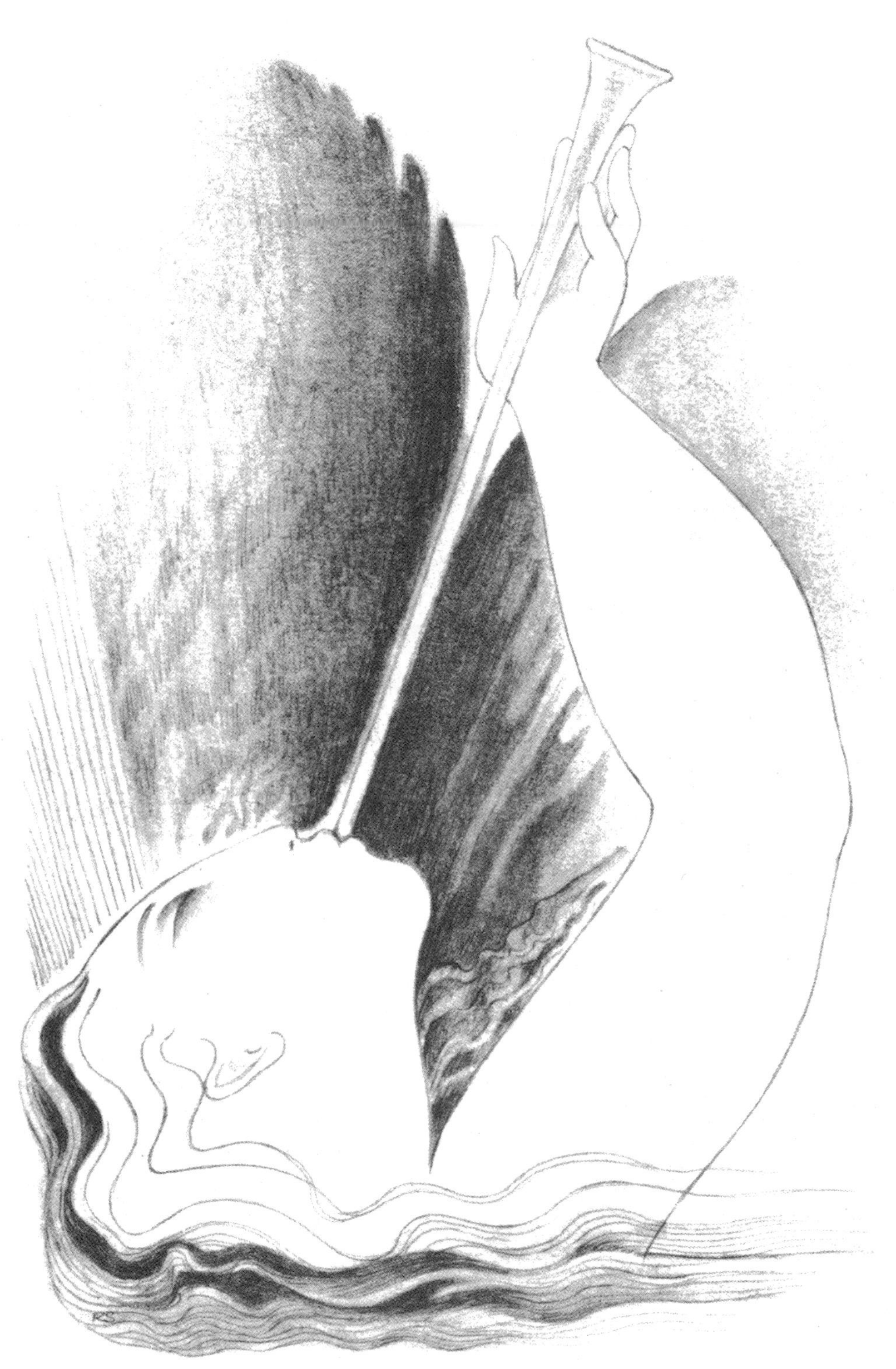

EXPANDING SENSATIONS

The secret
of shifting from calisthenics to *sensual meditations*
is this:
Immerse your awareness in a sensation
Then imagine the sensation expanding
from its center outward
throughout your whole body and energy field

These instructions are simple
To follow them is not easy
Expanding Sensations requires
an integration of mind and body
It is as if we place our whole being
in the center of a sensation
In a sense, we become it

We accomplish this centering and expanding with a gentle concentration. However, thoughts may intrude into our awareness. We then acknowledge to the thought that it exists and return our awareness to the sensation.

There is no necessity to stay with any one sensation. Whenever we become aware of another predominant sensation, we can bring our awareness to that sensation and expand it.

With the first experimentations it may seem like "nothing is happening." Remember that we are exploring subtle qualities. As we relax and tune into our body more, we will begin to discover a world that we often overlook in everyday life.

Special times for Expanding Sensations are after a breathing meditation, during and after a self-massage, and after giving or receiving a nurturing ceremony.

An Application

Generally allowing ten to fifteen minutes, lying or sitting with eyes closed, and without interruptions, take a tour through your body.

Begin at the feet and gradually come up the entire body to the top of the head.

Expanding Sensations

Starting at one foot, locate a sensation and expand it for a few moments. Then allow your awareness to move up to the ankle, find another sensation, and expand it.

And so on like this:

calf, knee, thigh, hip
other leg similarly
pelvic floor, mid abdomen, upper abdomen
one side of chest, other side of chest
one hand, wrist, forearm, elbow, upper arm, shoulder
other arm similarly
back of neck, throat
jaw, cheeks, eyes, temples, forehead, center of head
and finally the top of head

You could locate and expand one or more sensations in each section. The sections could be small or large. Be open to the possibility that the sensations that you are *locating* are often subtle.

Sometimes it is as though your awareness just stops at a place, and thus by having your attention there, you become aware of the aliveness that is already there.

This is often a delightful, sensual journey. Use it anytime you would like to calm your body/mind.

SELF-MASSAGE

In self-massage
we re-contact
we re-member
Self-massage is a body-appreciation ceremony
It is for aches and pains
It is for pleasure

You can give yourself a quickie any time, while driving the car, watching TV, or sitting in a business conference. All you do is put pressure on a point and stroke or squeeze while you are doing the other activities.

However, when we keep part of our attention on another activity, we may not reap the full benefit of the massage. When you are ready for a special treat, try a thirty- to sixty-minute ceremony of concentrated self-massage such as the following.

Self Massage

This structure can be modified extensively to apply to individual situations. The single most important factor is that you set aside the time for this ceremony to occur. You, in effect, make an appointment with yourself. An excellent time is before going to sleep.

Whenever and wherever you have the ceremony, be in a place that is warm, without TV and other distractions and interruptions. This may require making arrangements with household partners.

Begin, if you wish, with a bath or shower. Then settle onto a comfortable place such as your bed. Next apply a little oil or lotion to your hands. (Add more oil as necessary.)

Begin to touch yourself. To go more deeply inward, close the eyes. Never rush or be abusive with the touching. Allow an attitude of exploration. If the automatic pilot is on while squeezing here and pushing there, you will miss great benefits and joys.

The key is to continuously place your attention in the sensation created by each touch. This sensory response becomes your meditation. And rather than apply a planned sequence of strokes to your body, let your body tell you what it wants next. Sometimes you will find a place that *hurts so good.* Sometimes emotion will come up. You are always exploring. Your inner response is your compass.

There are many ways to touch yourself. Up and down, full-hand stroking connects different areas. You can make small circles with the finger and thumb pads. You can also put fair amounts of pressure with the finger or thumb pads. With this pressure, you might slide along grooves between the muscles or bones. When applying a lot of pressure, move slowly.

Gently pounding with the fists, tapping with the fingertips, or slapping with your palms are great for stimulation. And light feather strokes with your fingertips or nails are a delight.

Mix these strokes as you desire. Lingering at some places, just stroking over others, allow the massage to unfold itself.

Sometimes you may select only one section, such as your face. Or if you want to massage your whole body, the feet are generally a good starting place. Be sure to include inside the ears, under the arms, the genitals, perhaps inside the mouth and the nose.

Once you complete the self-massage, rest and Expand Sensations. It is almost like two massages — the first with the hands, the second with the mind.

Then if you go to sleep for the night after this, notice how your body feels the next morning.

Until we can truly appreciate
our own body and senses
we may find that instead of pleasuring another
we are only acting out a boring routine

If ceremony is to have meaning
it is to come out of our own aliveness
If we are to celebrate
we must truly appreciate the vehicle
through which we experience our celebration

9 ENERGY DANCE
Mutual Meditations

Striving for pleasure
prevents tasting the subtle nectars
Grasping,
we can not experience the gentle vibrations
of love, joy, and inner peace

This chapter like the previous
is about becoming more aware
of the subtle qualities of pleasure
and developing a sense of ceremony
In the previous chapter
we soared solo
Here we join with a partner

None of the meditations/exercises/processes/games
require dexterity or practice
Simply enter with a willingness
to allow the sensations and feelings
to unfold as you give and as you receive
Choose a meditation that interests you and your partner
and explore

Relax
Linger
Discover

MAPPING

One of the greatest inhibitors
to the experience of pleasure
is our comparative mind
We assume that we know
what our partner likes
(which often is really a projection
of what we like)
And relying on our past experiences
we also assume that we know what we like now
Unfortunately, our assumptions
are not always correct
Mapping is a meditation to check our assumptions
and to discover new sensual realms

In Mapping, as in land surveying, we discover the highs and lows. It also serves as an important communication tool which can be adapted to any nurturing situation.

The form of the communication is like this: with a range of "plus three" to "minus three," we indicate the degree of desirability or undesirability of each sensation.

The communication can be verbal or manual. With the latter, one hand is the plus hand and the other is the minus hand. Displaying one, two, or three fingers indicates the degree. For zero, the neutral point, form a circle with the positive hand's thumb and index finger.

It is very important to remember Mapping is a rating of the sensation, not of the performance of the mapper. Also, there is a tendency for the neutral point to shift throughout the process. Since this is not a scientific study, allow this subjective variability to be OK.

Whole Body Mapping

To begin, the recipient lies front down. She/he can be nude or minimally clothed.

As the mapper, you initiate the touches on the upper back and map down to the feet. Then softly invite your partner to turn over. Here begin the mapping at the feet and come up the legs, torso, arms, and finally the neck and head.

There are some guidelines to follow in this Whole Body Mapping.

Mapping

Touch simply.

Touch only one location at a time.

And touch only small areas about six inches being maximum. When the touch is much longer, there might be a "plus two" at one part and a "minus one" at another.

Vary the direction, pressure, and type of touch.

If there is a minus response, avoid repeating that particular touch on that part of the body. Equally important, let go of any performance of giving your partner a "plus three."

For right now at least, you are surveying. A massage can come later.

Sometimes until a mapper has had a personal experience of being mapped, she/he might find it a little boring. Keep in mind that this is a valuable service to the recipient. It is also a great way to *turn on / tune in* the whole body.

Once a giver and receiver become familiar with the plus-three-to-minus-three method, Mapping feedback can be shared in any pleasuring experience as an occasional communication.

GAMES

Approach the next meditations
as gentle games
They vary from quiet movements
to delightful play
to energizing massages
Which one you choose
would depend on the mood

Rag Doll

This is a simple and beautiful meditation
teaching about letting go and surrender

Rag Doll

For us to be able to truly receive a gift from another
we must be able to surrender
In surrender
we choose
to be where we are
This is in contrast to submission
in which we *give in* or *give up*
to another's power
because we think we have no alternative

In this meditation
the recipient is a rag doll
thus, no thoughts
no expectations
no comparisons
and no muscular tension

As the giver, you approach the rag doll with *beginner's mind.* This is the first time you have ever seen a rag doll, and in your fascination, you want to discover what it is like. Exploring from this perspective, you might come to a wonderful, new appreciation of your partner.

Your discovery takes the form of randomly and slowly moving the recipient's arms, legs, and head. Sometimes there are gentle stretches. This is all done non-verbally and without rushing.

The recipient may have a tendency to help in lifting the limbs or to hold on to the muscles. If you notice this, softly invite her/him to take a fuller breath and upon exhaling to relax the muscles. If this breathing technique is ineffective, it is better to silently allow the recipient to remain tense than to try to verbally or manually force a relaxation.

First, invite the recipient to lie down and to close her/his eyes. Then select either arm to begin the meditation. Slowly and gently explore all possible movements in the fingers, wrist, elbow, and shoulder area.

After the first arm, continue for about five minutes on each appendage in a similar fashion with the other arm, then one leg, and then the other. On the legs, support the knee joint when lifting and lowering a bent leg so as to avoid *popping* the knee when you straighten the leg.

Next take your friend on a *space walk* by lifting and slowly moving both legs.

After lowering the legs, introduce similar lifting movements very slowly to the head and neck.

When you are ready, gracefully slide your fingers off the ends of the hair strands.

And to complete, letting your fingers be like feathers, gently slide your fingertips from the top of her/his head down off the fingertips. Then slide from the top of the head down off the tips of the toes.

What may be the most important part of this meditation is the experience following the movements. The slow and gentle movements have stimulated subtle sensations, and the recipient, most likely, is deeply relaxed.

Rest in silence
until your partner feels like coming back to Earth

Born Again

As with the Rag Doll
this meditation teaches
about letting go and surrender
In Born Again
it is as if you were a flower bud opening
to the warming light of the sun

Here the recipient, perhaps with shoes off, lies on one side and tenses up into a tight fetal position. Holding this tension for about ten seconds, she/he might recontact what *holding on* feels like. Then, remaining in the fetal position, she/he simply relaxes.

Now with palms and fingers, stroke gently every section of the recipient's body. As you do this, very, very gradually uncoil the contracted form. Focus much more on the stroking than on the unfolding.

Eventually your partner is lying flat on her/his back with the arms at the sides.

Take a final visual check to make sure there are no curves in the alignment.

Then give a feather stroke from the head down off the fingers and from the head down off the toes.

Silently relax as the recipient floats.

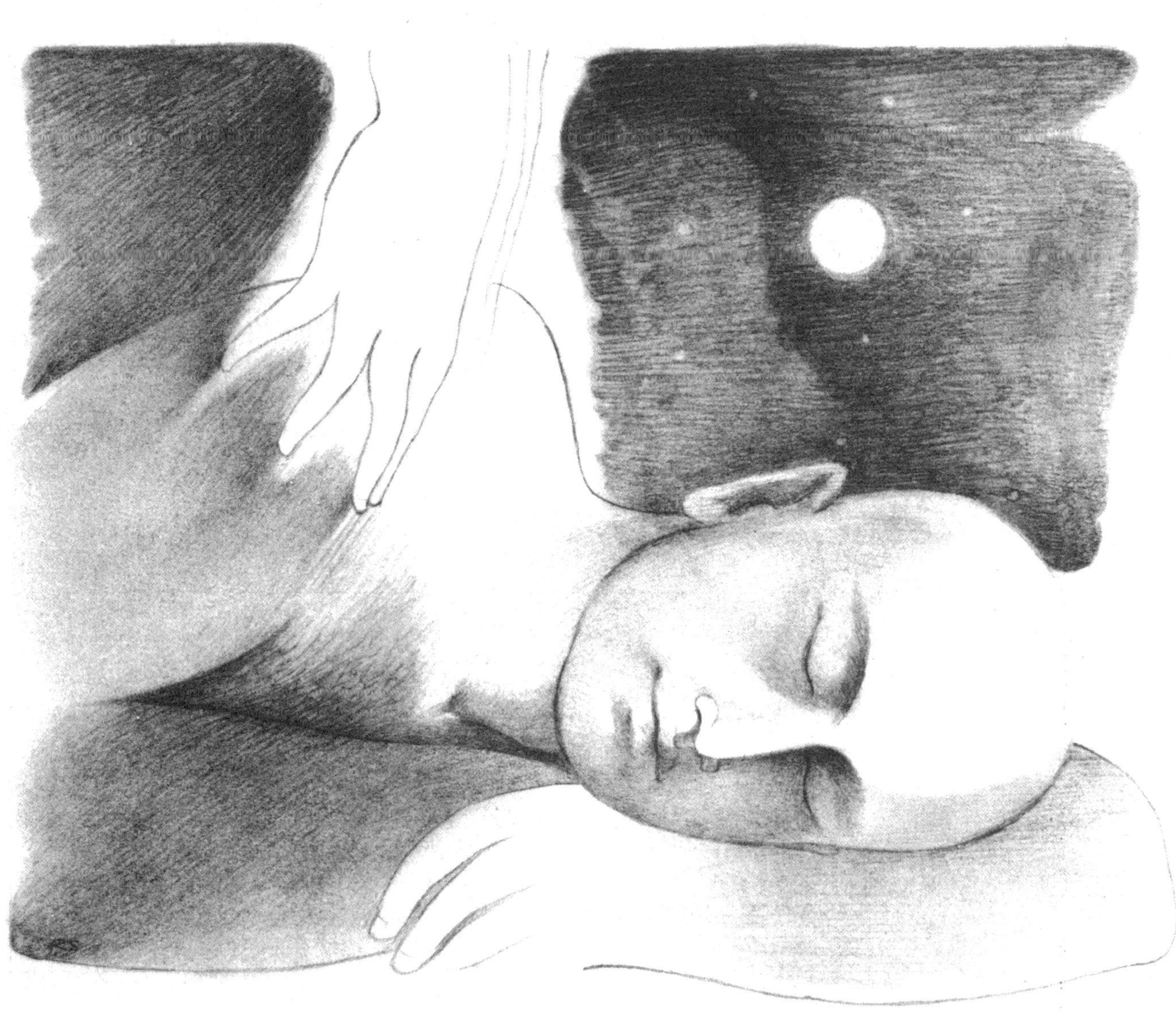

Bliss Caress

This would be a blissful follow-up
after a Whole Body Mapping
which would have already sensitized the skin surface

You can use one or more of these:
feathers, especially ostrich or peacock
silk scarves
furry fabrics
your hair or beard
brushes (be gentle if the bristles are hard)
plastic wrap
possibly your breath
your fingertips

For about five to twenty minutes, caress your partner by making long, flowing strokes all over her/his nude or partially nude body.

The number of substances is not important,
the gentle, connecting touches are

Grooming

In this delightful meditation we are borrowing from our furry cousins' grooming behaviors. And since we can use powder here, Grooming is an alternative to oil massage.

First, add a powder, such as corn starch, over all of one side of your nude or partially nude partner. Sprinkling the powder like gentle rain creates a special sensation in itself. (If no powder is available, you can still do this meditation.)

Then *groom* your friend with rapid hand movements in the following manner. With your thumb on one side and the fingers on the other side of a section of skin, rapidly and gently squeeze them together and lift up. The hands alternate with each other in rapid succession. In some areas, such as the thighs, you will probably see a ripple effect on the skin.

Gradually go up and down both sides of the recipient's body. On the face, throat, breasts, and genitals, be very gentle and a little slower.

If your hands become tired, you can slow down or feather stroke with your fingertips for a while.

A nice addition after Grooming is to caress your partner with about two feet of plastic wrap. Slide the edge across the skin. Notice how it statically clings to the skin.

Hair Brushing

Perhaps sitting in the sun or by a fireplace
slowly brush or comb through your partner's hair
If you wish to be more elaborate
you could shampoo first

Maybe lullaby or hum
as you brush

Slap Happy

This is *the energizer.* It is fantastic after driving or traveling for many hours or when you need to wake up.

Before beginning, the giver removes rings and watch; the recipient, any dangling earrings.

Then the standing recipient spreads her/his feet about shoulder distance apart and bends forward at the waist. It is best to let the knees bend a little and let the head and arms dangle toward the floor.

Now as the giver, *slap* your friend into a happy state. Standing from behind, begin slapping on the muscles on each side of the spine. It is usually best to totally avoid the bony part of the spine. Use the fleshy part of the little-finger side of your hands. You can also use the palms slightly cupped or the little-finger sides of your fists. It is best to alternate the hands: one goes down while the other goes up.

The amount of pressure on different parts of the body will vary from person to person. Be on the conservative side until the recipient indicates that more intensity is preferable.

After the back, slap with your palms on one leg at a time. Do this all the way down to the toes and back up. On the legs both hands can slap at the same time rather than in an alternating manner. Also be very careful to avoid the scrotum. In this bent-over position, the scrotum is much closer to your hands than you might imagine.

Next slap on the back area until you come to the arms.

On each arm, follow a similar pattern as on the legs.

Return to the back, this time standing at the recipient's head. Now focus on the upper back and shoulders. Gradually move to the scalp. Here briskly slide your finger pads back and forth but without much pressure. Increase the speed for a bit. Then suddenly lift your hands off. Voilà! The sudden ending is a sweet energetic thrill.

ENERGY

In a sensual ceremony
many subtle vibratory qualities
come to consciousness
The following meditations
aid in recognizing these qualities

To explore energy
it is best to enter with a relaxed attentiveness
and a willingness to try something new

Spoon Breathing

In Spoon Breathing
we combine touch with unison breathing
This is an especially intimate way
to share some quiet moments together
Try beginning or ending a ceremony this way

First your partner lies down on her/his side with the knees pulled forward a little for balance. Then also on your side, snuggle in closely behind. Your lower arm

Spoon Breathing

can be pointing upward, perhaps with a pillow or a folded towel placed between the arm and the head. If this position is uncomfortable, place your lower arm between yourself and your partner. Your upper arm rests on your partner's upper arm.

It is important not to tense the muscles by holding your partner. Simply relax and let your bodies melt together.

Once you become comfortable, tune into and follow your partner's breathing, matching the inhalation and the exhalation. This may at first seem awkward, but usually after a minute or so, it becomes natural.

For the purposes of this meditation, your partner can breathe in one of two ways. The first is to breathe as usual without any attempted alteration of pace or volume. The second method is to take slower and fuller breaths. This latter pattern seems more likely to enhance the experience of deep relaxation and subtle energy flows. Either way can be enjoyable.

Without watching the time, you might try this for ten minutes or longer. If sleep occurs, allow it. And if anything becomes a strain or a hassle, forget about the breathing and lie there cuddling.

Aura Massage

Here we bring our attention
to the energy fields around the recipient's physical body
Sometimes referred to as an aura
these energy fields are quite subtle
When we are calm and centered
we are more likely to become aware of them

Heart-to-Hand Breath

While it is not necessary to begin an aura massage with the Heart-to-Hand Breath, starting this way is an excellent preparation.

With your eyes closed, sitting or standing behind your reclining partner's head, bring your hands up to about the height of your heart.

Your palms are facing each other, about six inches apart. Your elbows are at your sides and your shoulders are relaxed.

When you inhale, imagine the breath coming into your heart center from all directions. In the exhalation, imagine the breath flowing from the heart to the shoulders, to the arms, and out the hands.

Repeat this combined breathing and visualization for twenty-five to fifty breaths.

By the end of this breathing meditation, you are more likely to have an inner calmness and your hands feel energized.

Energy Sensing

Next bring your hands from about six inches to one-half inch above your partner's head. Be careful not to physically touch the skin as that would be a predominating sensation.

Now slowly move your hands above the surface, using them as sensing devices. *Listen* with them. There might be humming, tingling, magnetic pushing or pulling, warmth or coolness. These may vary over different locations.

A slower movement is often necessary to become aware of the subtle vibrations. And you may find that the backs of your hands are a little more sensitive to sensing the different qualities of energy.

Continue the sensing around your partner's head and any other part of the body for several minutes before beginning the aura massage. (Actually you have already been massaging the aura, though your attention has initially been on your own sensing.)

An Aura Massage

Still without touching the physical body, begin to massage the energy field. There are several theories about what to do with this energy. For our purposes here, we allow ourself to be like a child again and pretend. Here simply play.

Move your hands as if you are polishing or combing the energy field. You can fluff it up or swirl it. Still moving slowly enough to sense the energy, allow your intuition or imagination to guide you. If you are willing to pretend, this can be a fun experience.

Maybe play with the aura massage for five to thirty minutes.

Afterward remain silent and allow the recipient to relax.

Whenever she/he returns to the physical world, share with each other about the experiences.

LAYING ON OF HANDS

Laying on of hands is an ancient ritual
While most often associated
with healing and religious rites
it is also a valuable part of sensual ceremonies
A touch that is still
and that conveys presence
can communicate feelings of love and care
far more deeply than most words

How we lay our hands
is more important
in this meditation
than *where*
Actually, *resting on of hands*
is a more accurate denotation

When you begin a laying on of hands, you might imagine that your hands are like an autumn leaf, descending in slow motion to rest on the earth. The autumn leaf has no expectations. It is not in a hurry. When it touches the earth, all it can do is rest there — simply be there.

To complete a laying, reverse this process, also in slow motion.

Entering and leaving the energy field in this manner is a non-verbal way of asking permission. It indicates a reverence. If we allow ourself to be as the autumn leaf without demands and without performance, we will nourish a deep sense of trust and connection.

You can give a whole *massage* with just a series of laying on of hands. Or you can add them as a part of a more inclusive nurturing meditation. One to five minutes in each position is usually sufficient.

Helmet

From behind the recipient's head, rest your palms so that your thumbs are side by side with the thumb pads on the middle of the forehead and your fingers are on the temples.

The helmet is also an especially nurturing way to begin a facial massage.

Third Eye and Navel

The *third eye* refers to an area approximately in the center of the forehead just above the eyebrows. Often we can feel a concentrated energy here.

While at your partner's side, make both of your hands into a relaxed fist shape. Then extend your thumbs, one toward the third eye, the other toward the navel. Very, very slowly allow your thumbs to descend to about a quarter inch above the third eye and navel.

Perhaps after about thirty seconds there, allow them to lightly touch the skin beneath.

Abdomen and Forehead

From beside your reclining partner, lay one of your palms over the third eye area and the other palm over the abdomen, a couple of inches below the navel. You might find that the energy flows more intensely when the palm's center is over the body's midline.

Tantric Laying On Of Hands

Here your awareness focuses on your middle fingers even though your whole palm touches.

Your upper hand rests so that the palm is on the recipient's forehead and your middle finger is at the center top of the head. This place was a fontanel, or *soft spot*, when we were babies.

Your other hand rests so that your middle finger touches the perineum, the area just between the anus and genitals. You may first need to separate your partner's thighs a little. Then if necessary, you would first use your upper hand to lift the scrotum and penis so that your lower hand can be in fuller contact with the pelvic floor.

As in the rest of this series, your hands are simply resting in place rather than applying pressure or movement.

Feet

Standing or sitting at your partner's feet, rest your fingers on top of the feet while your thumbs curve around, inside, to the underside in the arches.

This is also a wonderful way to conclude a full body massage.

These are only five specific positions
from many possibilities
Explore any intuitive inclination
And remember that your attentiveness
is more important
than where you actually touch

CHANTING

Chanting can nurture
Chanting can stimulate
subtle energies

Chanting

Which chant you use
is not important for these meditations
Any syllable or series of soothing syllables
is perfect
As a suggestion
try *OM* or *AUM*

There are at least two ways you can use chanting in a sensual ceremony. Either could open or close a ceremony or be a whole ceremony.

Together

The first is to chant in conjunction with your partner.

Here you sit closely and facing your partner. It might be helpful to have eyes closed to eliminate visual distractions. After being aware of your breathing for a minute or so, begin to chant together.

The chant itself could be continuous, each taking a breath when necessary. Or you could chant and then inhale in unison with your partner.

The intention here is to merge the sounds and energies. After a period of time, perhaps twenty minutes or longer, there may be a sense of Oneness.

Solo

Almost as if lullabying, you chant as your partner reclines beside you. This can be a very nurturing moment.

Here the chant might be melodic rather than a single tone. If you are not accustomed to chanting or singing in front of another, it might be a little scary at first. How well you are chanting, however, is not important. What is important is that you are truly sharing yourself.

When to chant is often an intuitive choice. One special time is when pouring water on your partner in a bath. Another is at the ending of a massage.

Conclusion

The willingness to experiment
is the key to these meditations
When we discover
our ability to experience subtle vibratory qualities
within each sensation and each feeling
our relationship to our body and our partner
will be immensely enriched

The *tantric explorations*
of these last two chapters
are valuable preparations for The Secret Garden Ceremony
They are special means for rediscovering
ourself and our partner

To be able to experience pleasure
in a way that neither craves nor condemns the body
is a celebration

EPILOGUE

While techniques and suggestions
provide practical guidelines
they still are only guidelines
They are form
not essence

When we open
to inner beauty
When we bring
presence to our self-expression
we approach essence

Michelangelo once was asked
why God favored him with such special talent
to sculpture forms into marble

Michelangelo responded
it was not his talent
to sculpture into the stone
Rather
his mastery
was in the ability
to see the beauty
that God had already created
in the marble

Michelangelo would then simply uncover
that beauty
by smoothing away the rough edges

In tantric sensual ceremony
we bring our attention
to sensory and feeling experiences
We slow down
so that we become aware of subtleties
We discover
the beauty
beneath the rough edges
We nurture
the senses in gentleness

The heart is touched
and we experience joy